The Big J vs

Janine Booth is a Marxist, trade unionist,
member, socialist-feminist, supporter of Workers' Liberty,
autistic, bi, author, poet, disaffected middle-aged woman
and Peterborough United fan.
She works on London Underground and is active in the
RMT trade union, having previously represented its London
Transport members on the union's National Executive.
Janine is Chair of the union's Disabled Members' Advisory
Committee and a member of the TUC Disabled Workers'
Committee. She writes and delivers trade union training,
particularly on equalities issues, and speaks widely on
socialist politics, history, disabled people's rights, autism
and neurodiversity.
Janine lives in Hackney, East London, with her partner,
kids and various pets.

Also by the author

Poetry

Mostly Hating Tories [1]

The 3Rs: *Ranting Rhyming Revolting* [1]

'16 – The Age of Discontent: *A Ranting, Rhyming, Revolting Review of the Year* [1]

Disaffected Middle-Aged Women [2]

Non-poetry

Comrades and Sisters: *Women and the Struggle for Liberation* [3]

Guilty and Proud of It: *Poplar's Rebel Councillors and Guardians 1919-1925* [4]

Plundering London Underground: *New Labour, Private Capital and Public Service 1997-2010* [4]

Autism Equality in the Workplace: *Removing Barriers and Challenging Discrimination* [5]

Minnie Lansbury: *Suffragette, Socialist, Rebel Councillor* [6]

Published by

[1] Hastings Press, [2] Roundhead Publications, [3] Workers' Liberty (eBook), [4] Merlin Press, [5] Jessica Kingsley Publishers, [6] Five Leaves Publications

THE BIG J
VS
THE BIG C

issues, experiences and poems
in the battle against breast cancer

JANINE BOOTH

Flapjack Press

www.flapjackpress.co.uk

Exploring the synergy between performance and the page

Published in 2019 by Flapjack Press
Salford, Gtr Manchester
www.flapjackpress.co.uk

ISBN 978-1-9161479-1-1

Photographs copyright © Natansky where credited
www.natansky.co.uk
All other photographs courtesy of the author

Cover design by Paul Neads
www.paulneads.co.uk
Adapted from an idea by the author

Printed by Imprint Digital
Upton Pyne, Exeter, Devon
imprintdigital.com

FSC **MANCHESTER**
City of Literature

*To my family, friends, comrades and
health workers who helped me through.*

CONTENTS

Foreword *by Kate Smurthwaite*   *10*

I: DETECTION AND DIAGNOSIS   **15**
Tests on My Breasts   18
Responses   30
Tumour Humour: Titter Ye Not   33
21 October 1966   37

II: SURGERY   **40**
Lucky Me   47
It's Not Me, It's You   49
BBC: Big Breast Cancer   51

III: BETWEEN TREATMENTS   **57**
Waiting   57
Battle Scars   61
Brown Toast   70

IV: RADIOTHERAPY   **73**
Cancer Can't Write Poetry, But Poetry Can Write Cancer   80
Roadside Breakdown   83

V: GETTING OVER IT   **88**
Telling Time   94
Disinfected Middle-Aged Women   106

VI: KEEPING CANCER AT BAY   **110**
Haiku: Menopausal Dryness   117
Eyes on the Prize   119
Oophorectomy   121
Hot Flush   126
A Warm Hand   130
Homage to Hospitals   133

"[The NHS] will survive for as long as there are folk willing to fight for it."
Aneurin Bevan
Labour MP, Minister for Health 1945-1951

FOREWORD

I first met Janine at Tolpuddle Martyrs Festival, which, if the anti-establishment ever decided to compile a Who's Who, is presumably where they would start. We shared an afternoon stage in a wonky marquee and I was blown away. Poetry was not something I had ever considered putting on at my midnight show at the Edinburgh Fringe, but I was sure my crowd would make an exception for Janine. A few weeks later I was proved entirely right.

Since then, I've unfortunately worked with Janine many times. Not unfortunately because it's anything but a pleasure to work with her, quite the opposite. For fans of a good oxymoron I'd be happy to call her work 'consistently surprising'. But unfortunately, because if you see one of us handing a microphone to the other you can be pretty sure something is rotten in the borough of Hackney, corporate greed, devastating cuts, unfair treatment, and whoever is sorting the mess out needs a fundraiser.

It's trite to say cancer affects us all at some point. In fact, it affects us all every day, from the pang of worry as we put out *definitely the last* cigarette to the absence, noticed or unnoticed, of those who have died too early.

Janine's book entered my life a few weeks after my boyfriend's mum, Lucia, had been diagnosed with breast cancer. Flavio and I had been discussing our schedules and when he would fly out to Italy to accompany her to treatments and consultations. Halfway through reading the book I spent four hours in the Marie Curie hospice in Liverpool with my friend, the comedy promoter Tim Miles, who lost his life to bone cancer about a week later.

I'm forty-three years old and so far in my life I've lost a childhood friend, Clare, to leukaemia, an aunt, Jean, to bone cancer, a grandmother, Em, to breast cancer, an agent, Mick, to stomach cancer, a college friend, Dan, to lung cancer, a close friend's wife, Helen, to a rare blood cell cancer and so many more. And now Tim.

Cancer is everywhere, and we need to talk about it. About the treatment process and options, the politics of medical provision, the emotions, the right and wrong ways to offer solidarity, the sad bits, the funny bits and the terrible inconvenience of it. A daunting task. So it came as no surprise to hear Janine had stepped right up.

I picked up this book expecting to be educated, entertained and amused. I was also hoping to pick up some information that would help me offer support to those in my life who are affected by cancer. I put it down having ticked all of those boxes. But it's also done something else. It's reminded me that the NHS is quite literally the best thing there is in the entire world. I hope it does the same for you. We must never stop fighting for it.

Kate Smurthwaite
Comedian & Activist
April 2019

THE BIG J
vs
THE BIG C

I

DETECTION AND DIAGNOSIS

11 September 2016 : That Can't Be Right

It was a Sunday evening and I was standing in front of the bedroom mirror doing my regular breast checks. The mirror is actually the door of my wardrobe, and if I stand facing it, I can get a decent view as well as a good feel. No lumps or bumps, no worries.

Having finished my inspection, it occurred to me that whilst I was standing there, I would stretch my triceps. I reached my right arm across my left shoulder, put my left hand on my right elbow and pulled it towards me, and felt a lovely muscle stretch. And as I did so, I noticed something a little odd in the mirror: the lower part of my right breast moved up, causing an indentation to appear. It looked like it was being sucked up by a vacuum inside my boob.

That can't be right, I thought. Returning my arm to its usual place, the strange dent disappeared. Did that mean it was OK after all?

I repeated the exercise and, sure enough, up came the indentation again. I did the same with my left arm and no unusual crater appeared. I summoned my partner, John, and repeated the performance for him. He agreed that no, that can't be right.

15 September 2016 : GP Appointment

I arranged a GP appointment as soon as possible, which meant as soon as the GP surgery's phone was not engaged, which meant the Thursday of that week.

I am in and out of that surgery like a dog at a fair, as Lancastrians say, so I imagined the doctor thinking *Oh heck, it's her again. What now?*

He had already seen my legs, my eyes, my ankles, my sinuses, my cervix, my strange skin patches and the darkest recesses of my mind, so perhaps my boobs would just complete the picture. I visualised him reassuring me that no, it was nothing to worry about and yes, it was better to be safe than sorry and of course, it was no trouble, and then as soon as I shut the door behind me, banging his forehead on his desk in between the prescription pad and the stethoscope and silently screaming to God to save him from me.

But no. My GP was pleasant and professional, and took me seriously. I told him my story and he examined me while a woman staff member stood by to ensure that everything was above board. Although he could not find a lump, he could see the strange shape when I showed him, and referred me to the breast clinic at the local Homerton Hospital.

So, here is an important tip: *You are not just looking for lumps*. There are other signs of breast cancer too, illustrated very well by Breast Cancer Worldwide's #KnowYourLemons illustration. Mine was like the lemon second from the left on the top row. Yours might be like any of the others. You really need to look up the graphic to see what I mean.

22 September 2016 : Breast Clinic

Said appointment was just a week later, a pleasant surprise given how long I had had to wait for previous referrals for complaints such as allergies and a broken ankle. I went on my own, and did not even tell John.

The appointment was at 09:40, and I made the fifteen-minute walk from home to the hospital feeling pretty calm. It is a pleasant stroll through central Hackney, past the historic Gibbon's Corner, across the Narroway shopping street, past the historic St. Augustine's Tower, across the historic St. John's Churchyard, past the historic Sutton House and simultaneously under and past the thoroughly modern City Academy. I have walked it many times before, to the hospital when illness or childbirth struck, and to the various attractions en route on more leisurely occasions.

I had decided that I probably did have breast cancer. I knew that it might be something more benign, but that was not very likely, and if I held on to that hope, then I risked shock and disappointment. If I accepted that it was cancer, then I would get either a pleasant surprise or a treatment plan.

I arrived at the desk and the receptionist told me to sit in the waiting room with the ~~udders~~ others. The breast clinic felt welcoming and caring; without exception, everyone was friendly and kind. I did not have to wait long before going in to see the consultant, Doctor Parvanta, who examined me and found a lump. She evidently has more finely-tuned fingers than either myself or the GP. She sent me for an immediate mammogram.

A nurse escorted me to the appropriate suite of rooms, and gave me a gown and a cubicle in which to change. Once gowned, I was led into the mammography room. The mammogram involved me standing in a very exact posture next to a machine and hoisting my boob onto a table, then a transparent plate descending on top of it and squashing it out into a vast mass of boob (if you have vast boobs; presumably a smaller mass if you have smaller ones). Mine looked like a huge piece of dough waiting to be kneaded into a gigantic loaf. Once the correct position was confirmed, the machine delivered its X-rays and made its image of the inside of my breast. The whole procedure took only a few minutes and was painless and non-invasive. It may have been uncomfortable, but I was too busy finding it funny to notice. And no, my breast did not get stuck: the machine was not a booby trap.

The mammogram having shown the lump, I then needed an ultrasound scan to take another look. I had experience of this procedure, from pregnancies and from when I had an ovarian cyst many years ago. Again, this was painless and non-invasive. As I lay horizontal and comfortable, the radiographer applied gel to my breast then moved a hand-held ultrasound probe around my gelled skin. The probe sent high-frequency sound waves into my breast, which bounced back and created a moving image on a screen. Sometimes the radiographer needed to push the probe into the flesh a little firmly, but other than that, there was very little discomfort.

The ultrasound confirmed the presence of the lump, so I needed an immediate biopsy. I was surprised and impressed, although a little nervous. I had expected that if tests were needed, an appointment would be fixed. But no, they just cracked on with it.

Biopsy involves removing actual pieces of the tumour, so despite my circumspection and good humour up to this point, I have to admit that this test was unpleasant and painful. The radiographer applied disinfectant wipes, then a local anaesthetic with a needle, then made a small cut and inserted a big needle containing the biopsy kit. This device was like a staple gun: I lost count of the number of times it clicked and I winced as it bit off bits of my tumour for the docs to chew over.

When it was finally done, the nurse put a small plaster over the needle wound, and I went back to the cubicle to replace gown with clothes. Back in her office, consultant Doctor P told me that although only the biopsy result could confirm it – and that would take a week or two – she was pretty sure that I had cancer: she could not imagine what else it would be. I appreciated her honesty. She also said that the NHS could treat it, and that breast cancer survival rates are very good these days. I appreciated this even more.

I would be back on 4 October for the test results.

Tests on My Breasts

Take this basket into this stall
Waist upwards: off with it all
On with the gown
(No, the other way round)
This is what we're going to do
OK with you?

Into the room, off with the gown
Lift your breast and lay it down
On this plate, stand like this
Shoulder back, hand on hip
This might squeeze a little bit

Finally fine with the lie of the breast
Foot pedal pressed
Down comes the see-through plate
Squash and spread to investigate
Look away
From examining rays

A few more seconds and that one's done
Repeat it for the other one
Lift, lay
There, stay
Feet, stand
Hip, hand
Done both breasts
Need more tests

Ultrasound, inside inspecting
Remember the times when I was expecting
But that was looking at a lump of life
That was benign
Don't know if it is this time
Squidgy gel on the hand-held scanner
Perfectly pleasant bedside manner

Moves it around, looks on a screen
Finds the best view on the scanning machine
Overboob, underboob, armpits too
Look at the lymph nodes, look for a clue
Looking concerned
What have we learned?

We need a biopsy – What, today?
Yes, straightaway
Lie down, still naked from the waist up
Unsupported 42J cup
Needle ready, local anaesthetic
Calm and kind and sympathetic

A prick, a cut – this might hurt a bit
Then insert the biopsy kit
Then you'll feel a series of clicks
I'll warn you each time
Thanks, that's fine.
Now. Click. Again
Some discomfort, not really pain

Now. Click. Again
Pain that time
Distract my mind
By reciting rhymes
Telling stories
Hating Tories
Now. Click. Again

Now. Click. Again.
Lost count
Indefinite amount
Cleaned and dried
Adhesive strips applied
Then dressing
The wound then myself
No more guessing
Or supposing
Diagnosing

Mind the Gap : Cancer and Class ... or 'The Lumpen Proletariat' ...

Let's have a look at those survival rates, and in particular, variations
according to social class.

Over recent decades, UK cancer death rates have fallen significantly.
They began falling in the late 1980s, and by the mid-noughties had
fallen by 17% (*Cancer and Health Inequalities: an introduction to
current evidence*, Cancer Research-UK, 2006). More people than ever
before are surviving cancer, with 78% of women in England and Wales

still alive ten years after their breast cancer diagnosis (2010-11; cancerresearchuk.org/health-professional/cancer-statistics/statistics-by-cancer-type/breast-cancer).

But there are still big differences between cancer outcomes depending on how wealthy you are. Economic inequality – the polite term for 'class divisions' – is linked to 19,000 cancer deaths per year (Cancer Research-UK science blog, 29 May 2014).

A decade ago, the *Daily Telegraph* sounded the alarm to its affluent readership that the 'middle classes [were] 'more likely to develop breast and skin cancer'' (25 September 2008). The article reported statistical differences in the incidence of various cancers between the poorest fifth of the population and the wealthiest fifth, the latter being a somewhat odd definition of the 'middle class' referred to in its headline. If middle means top, I wonder what the newspaper would call the actual middle. Although the report cited in the article only showed statistical correlation between social class and incidence of these cancers rather than the causes of this, the Torygraph was quick to declare the reasons, stating that 'career women delaying having children and exposing themselves more to the sun on foreign holidays are thought to be behind the gap'. There is some consolation for the well-to-do, though: their lower-income fellow human beings are more likely to get lung or cervical cancer, 'because people from poorer classes are more likely to smoke and skip smear tests'.

A balanced assessment of the study on which the *Telegraph* based its report (e.g. NHS choices, 'Cancer and socioeconomic group', 26 September 2008) – rather than a glance at a headline – shows the gaps weighing rather more heavily on poorer women. Although the least deprived (i.e. the wealthiest) fifth of women were 0.15 times (i.e. 15%) more likely to develop breast cancer, the most deprived fifth of women were 2.7 times as likely (i.e. 170% more likely) to get lung cancer than the top fifth were. Moreover, although poorer women were less likely to get breast cancer, they were 6% more likely to die from it.

Allow me to ponder for a moment on the *Telegraph*'s choice of the word 'skip' to describe poorer women not attending cervical smear tests. Although in this case, the word does not literally mean 'dance gaily through flowery summer meadows', it does project a notion of a carefree, reckless decision not to attend. Research shows that working-class women are less likely to attend cervical smear tests and as these results show, breast screening:

• Women who own their own car and women who own their own house are more likely to attend breast screening (Cancer Research science blog, 17 June 2009).

• 31% of women with manual or routine occupations reported irregular or non-attendance at breast screening, compared to 17% of professional or managerial women (CR-UK, 2006).

• In my own, very working-class, home borough of Hackney, East London, only 58.2% of women aged 53-70 attend breast cancer screening, way lower than the English average of 75.4% (Cancer Research website, local statistics, accessed 19 April 2017).

But are they wantonly 'skipping' screening appointments, or is there something else going on? Researchers tend to prefer the term 'lower uptake' to 'skipping', and have variously found that:

• Most health information is text-based (CR-UK, 2006), so it is less accessible to people who are less literate or whose first language is not English, who are more likely to be working-class or poor.

• Women who own their own car find it easier to get to their breast screening appointment (presumably by driving their car).

• Whilst 94% of the most affluent women are aware of breast cancer screening, only 84% of the most deprived women are (CR-UK, 2006).

• Some women do not attend because they are too busy (healthtalk.org, 'Reasons for not attending breast screening', accessed 19 April 2017).

Perhaps less measurably, it may be that working-class women's lives are more demanding, more stressful, less supported, and consequently more liable to see 'optional extras' such as cancer screening slip through life's net. With an estimated 1,400 women's lives saved each year by the NHS's breast screening programme (CR-UK, 2006), disproportionately few of these saved lives are those of working-class and poor women.

Not only are poorer women less likely to take up screening, they are also less likely to recognise cancer symptoms, a combination which leads to later diagnosis, which in turn reduces the chances of survival. Women who live in deprived areas are more likely to be diagnosed with advanced breast cancer and less likely to survive for five years; women diagnosed at the earliest stage of breast cancer are twenty-six times more likely to survive than those diagnosed at the latest stage (CR-UK, 2006).

The wealthier a person is, the more that person tends to know about cancer risk factors, and the more likely they are to take measures to avoid risk, such as eating five portions of fruit and veg daily, taking physical exercise (CR-UK, 2006) and breastfeeding (*Factors associated with breastfeeding in England: an analysis by primary care trust*, BMJ Open, 2013).

So, working-class women live less healthy lives and are more likely to die from breast cancer than rich women. The statistics prove it. But why? The loathsome Margaret Thatcher once described poverty as a 'personality defect', and the equally loathsome Boris Johnson argued that some people are just too unintelligent to get on in life (Mail Online, 27 November 2013). Although few right-wing ideologues would state it in such a vulgar way, plenty believe that these inequalities arise from the inherent inferiority of the great unwashed. The poor are poor because they make poor choices.

Alternatively, perhaps the poor make poor choices because they have little choice because they are poor. Where serious research papers refer to 'lifestyle factors' in cancer outcomes, newspapers will often instead refer to 'lifestyle choices', a sleight of hand which subtly points the finger at the individual and strips their choices of their social context. In reality, we do make choices, and we are responsible for them, but we make those choices in circumstances not always within our control, and the less money we have, the further beyond our control those circumstances are.

Perhaps poorer people take less physical exercise not because they are lazy but because they cannot afford (the time or money) to join the local council's sports centre, let alone the tennis or rugby club. Perhaps the 'choice' to grab some fast food rather than browse the farmers' market for organic veg is a choice shaped by shortage of funds and time. Perhaps you 'skipped' the chance to be screened because you did not receive or understand the letter inviting you, or you could not get the time off work without losing wages you could not afford to lose. Some 'lifestyle factors' – for example, the 5% of breast cancers caused by exposure to carcinogenic factors at work (cancerresearchuk.org/health-professional/cancer-statistics/statistics-by-cancer-type/breast-cancer) – are not really 'choices' at all. And perhaps at a more subconscious level, the more pleasant and comfortable your life is, the more effort you will put in to preserve it.

Cancer Research UK does a valuable service in commissioning the research that gives us these facts – a service so valuable that it deserves to be carried out and funded by the government rather than relying on coffee mornings, sponsored sky-dives and funding from the private health industry. CR-UK also has many proposals for reducing the inequalities in cancer outcomes: more research; health promotion targeted at 'hard-to-reach' groups; communication training for health professionals; a drive to increase screening uptake amongst the most deprived groups; and more.

All these would be welcome. But isn't there a more obvious, more fundamental, more straightforward solution? If poverty increases your chances of dying of breast and other cancers, then surely the most effective measure would be to abolish poverty. If class divisions cause inequalities in cancer outcomes, then abolish the division of society into classes: remake society on an equal and co-operative footing. Obviously, advocating such radically common-sense ideas is beyond the remit of a charity. But it is not beyond the remit of me.

4 October 2016 : Diagnosis Day

My partner, John, took the news with concern but calm, and accompanied me to the appointment where I would find out for definite. It did not start auspiciously. I got the time wrong (I thought it was at 10:40; it was at 10:20) then spent ten minutes in a queue I did not expect to be there. *We will see if we can squeeze you in*, they said, and squeeze me in they did. I expected there was going to be a lot of squeezing in – and some squeezing out – over the next few months, because when I met the consultant, Doctor Parvanta, she confirmed that I had breast cancer. Not good, right? Sure, but I felt quite matter-of-fact about it.

It was better knowing, and being able to crack on with the treatment, than the last three weeks of not knowing but strongly suspecting. In any case, when something like this comes along, you do what you need to do, the outcome is whatever it is.

So, here are the facts that matter.

The lump was 2.5cm in diameter. I responded to this information by bending my thumb and declaring this as the distance from the bend to the tip. I learned this as a child, although I suspect that my thumb may have been smaller then. Still, it is about right.

It could have been there for a couple of months or a couple of years (the lump not my thumb): there is no way of knowing. I speculated as to whether it might have been found earlier if women under fifty got regular mammograms as women aged fifty-plus do, but the consultant explained that breast tissue is thicker and less scannable at younger ages, so it might not have been found. Yes, but it might have been. I felt rather cheated, as I was turning fifty a fortnight later, and there was a trial in progress giving mammograms to women from age 47. I wish I had been in that trial. Moreover, new digital mammograms are providing clearer images through the denser breast tissue of women under fifty.

The good news was that the cancer had (probably) not spread to my lymph nodes, the gateway to it spreading round my body. I say 'probably' because that would only be confirmed by the next week's MRI scan.

The particular cancer I had was ductal cancer, meaning that it was in the milk ducts, even though, having breastfed three babies, I was supposed to be less likely to get that. There is another type of breast cancer, known as nodular, or something like that. To be honest, my mind concentrated pretty well on information about what I had, but drifted somewhat when it came to what I did not have.

I asked what might have caused me to get breast cancer. I knew a little about risk factors, and speculated as to the influence one way or the other of my being overweight, and having had three children at the age of 32, 35 and 37. Doctor P replied, very firmly, 'You have just been unlucky.' My guilt evaporated.

There are those who argue that feminism causes cancer. Zoe Williams summarised this argument while unpicking it in 2007 (theguardian.com/world/2007/mar/28/gender.uk): 'Having children later – which is what happens if you are a feminist and you work – makes you more likely to get breast cancer. Not having children at all – which is what happens if you are a feminist and it is all about you rather than nurturing – makes you more likely to get breast cancer and ovarian cancer'. This does not sit well with the other common anti-feminist claim that feminists want women to 'have it all', because if that were true, we would be having children while pursuing careers, rather than postponing the former in order to do the latter. Perhaps the fact that delaying having kids has a positive impact on your finances is a crucial factor here, but that is caused not by feminism but by capitalism.

I got the basic information from the consultant and was then led away by the cancer nurse for a pep talk. Prem, said nurse, was very informative and supportive, running through the basics and giving me a book and her phone number.

It turned out that 2.5cm is big enough to not be small, if you get my drift. Together with it not having spread to the lymph nodes, this meant that the cancer was at Stage 2a. It also turned out that as well as having a Stage, my cancer also had a Grade. That concerned what the cells were like, which we would find out on further investigation. Prem's best quote was: 'If you're going to get cancer, breast cancer is the one to get'. Decent survival rates, you see. Phew.

The next step would be an MRI scan the following Tuesday. A quick question brought reassurance that the metal clip in my right eye socket (resulting from an unfortunate encounter with a stray firework eleven years previously) would not prevent me having the MRI. I had a fearful premonition of the machine sucking the titanium plate out of my socket and spinning it round like a pound coin you accidentally left in your trouser pocket when you loaded the washing machine.

The scan result would determine the course of treatment. It was likely to be surgery (lumpectomy) within four weeks, followed by none, one or more of the following: chemotherapy, radiotherapy, and a hormone tablet that you take for five years. And with that, diagnosis was done, and the fightback began. Farewell, Homerton Hospital – see you next week.

A tip: it can be a good idea to take a partner, friend or otherwise supportive person with you. This is partly for moral support, partly to ask the questions you forget to ask, but also so they can buy you a nice lunch afterwards. On the other hand, having said lunch at the café next to the local graveyard may not be everyone's cup of tea. Lovely veggie burgers, though.

Me and My Boobs

We go back a long way, my boobs and I. To roughly the late 1970s, when I was about twelve.

I didn't mind having none as a kid. I was much more interested in climbing trees, playing football and riding my bike, and boobs would have got in the way of that. I was not one of those girls who yearned for grown-up femininity and rehearsed for hours with make-up and dresses. The nearest I got was one occasion larking about with my mum, putting tangerines up my T-shirt to practise for when the real ones arrived. Oh, how we laughed. Little did we know then that within a few years, breasts the size of watermelons would take the place of those tangerines.

They started to grow – and they did not stop. By my late teens, I seriously wondered whether I lacked the hormone or whatever it is that tells them to grow no further. In my best Yoda voice, I told them that they must finish what they had started – not the defeat of the evil Empire, but their ceaseless expansion. Eventually, with or without the help of the Force, they did.

Since then, they have been my constant companions. In my younger adulthood, they ably assisted with nights out on the pull. They have been my own personal airbag, a buffer between me and anything in front of me, and a travelling pillow for various children, animals and friends. They fed my three babies and managed to do so without smothering them. Although they have cost me a small fortune in bras, and ruined my football career (which, to be fair, was also ruined by my never having seriously tried to have one), I love my boobs, I really do.

But now they were trying to kill me. Was this some sort of revenge for what I had put them through? Or could I look at it in a different way? Maybe something was attacking them, and through them, attacking me. It could still be me and my boobs versus the world.

Cancer, I hold you in similar contempt to those blokes who think it is OK to yell out of car windows or sidle up to me in the street to inform me that I have very large breasts because unless they had pointed that out, I obviously would not have known. You are not wanted, not funny, and you can get lost.

4 October 2016 : Telling People

When the nurse had given me the lump lowdown, she asked me if I had any questions. I did not want to ask about medical stuff – she and the consultant had already told me loads and the rest was in the book or on the end of a phone. So I blurted out pretty much the only question I cared about: *How do I tell my kids?*

The answer was much as I had expected: be honest and straightforward, do not panic or patronise them. What I was not expecting was another book: a superhero comic guide to breast cancer. Genius idea. That will be as useful to me as to my superyoungest, then aged 12 (the other two were 14 and 17). It is called *Medikidz Explain Breast Cancer*. Check it out.

Telling them was much easier than I feared. Just tell them straight. So I did. Any questions? Yes: 'Can I go out and play on the estate now?' Yes, off you go, son.

Kids are very resilient. Of course, there may be times when it bothers them more – not least when I am lying around post-surgery demanding that they bring me drinks, snacks and stuff to read. I warned them about this. Youngest replied: 'But you do that anyway, Mum.' Cheeky blighter.

Then there was the phone call to my parents. That made me sad. I think I would know how I would feel if any of my kids got this awful disease, even if they were nearly 50 and I was still around. (Tangentially, I do wonder why people so often say *I can't begin to imagine how people feel in* x *situation*. You can. Try.) My olds were both 79 and caring, loving people. I felt bad telling them rotten news. Not for the last time, I realised that I had to comfort other people as well as other people comforting me.

Then I had to tell work. My boss is a bloke and, nothing personal you know, I just did not want to discuss it with him. So I had arranged in advance that I would speak with another manager, a woman, who would keep my boss advised of the essentials. That was working out OK so far. Being a trade unionist, I know my rights, and I seriously doubted that my employer would try to deny me them!

If you get cancer, know this: you are explicitly defined as 'disabled' under the terms of the Equality Act from the moment you are diagnosed, whether or not you are suffering ill-health or any symptoms at all. This means that it is unlawful for your employer to discriminate against you, whether this is directly, or indirectly, related to some matter arising from your cancer, by harassing you, causing you a detriment for asserting your rights, or refusing to make reasonable adjustments for you. (We will look at these in more detail when I return to work post-treatment.)

There were a few more people to tell, not least my lifelong friend and fellow ranting poet Attila the Stockbroker, who had endured camera-up-the-knob treatment for bladder cancer of late, and whose mum survived breast cancer many years back. The pair of us were well aware of the enormous comic potential for boob and knob gags bouncing back and forth between us.

It remained only to tell the rest of the world via the trusty social media, and the dam burst under the wave of support and solidarity. I issued a list of rules:

1. It's OK to talk about it.
2. I may have to blow out of commitments I have made to do stuff over the next while, but don't assume I have done unless I tell you.

3. Boob jokes are fine. Sexist jokes are not. If you don't know the difference, shut up. (I'm working on my sense of tumour.)
4. Cancer is going to regret picking a fight with me.
5. Be nice to my family.
6. First poem on the subject to follow soon.
7. My birthday party goes ahead whatever.
8. Check your boobs regularly. Including you blokes.

Responses

I'm so sorry to hear that.
How awful.
I don't know what to say.

At least they caught it early.
Oh, they didn't?
I'm sure you'll still be OK.

My friend's got that.
She's having chemo –
Head down the toilet all day.

My mum had that. They gave her a year.
That was sixteen years ago –
She's still here!

My sister had that. She ignored it and it spread
Until it was too late.
She's dead.

Turmeric. Vitamins. Crystals.
No sugar. And filter your water –
There's a website by some guy …
You'll be fine, you're a fighter –

Because Spitfires never get shot down,
And boxers never die.
Do they?

Oh you poor thing.
You must cancel everything and rest.
It's for the best.

Sit down. I'll get you a tea.
No, no, I'll do that.
Don't you worry. Leave it to me.

Is that OK?
Are there any
Right words to say?

11 October 2016 : Maps of My Baps

It was Booby Tuesday, the day I would have an MRI scan. That's Magnetic Resonance Imaging, and it would produce a much more detailed image of my tumour and breast than the scans (mammogram and ultrasound) I had had so far. It would make maps of my baps.

I have had two MRIs before – one in 2005 of my brain when I was hit in the eye by a firework, and one as recently as 2015 of my broken ankle – so I knew the drill. Or at least, I thought I did. This one turned out to be a little different.

The books I took with me to keep myself entertained while waiting proved unnecessary, as I was seen straightaway. First I undressed – for an MRI, this included taking off my rings and removing my false eye. Then, once gowned, I ran through some questions with the nurse – previous operations, medical conditions, and so on. There was barely enough room on the form to fit it all in: the nurse managed it with the help of some sideways writing.

The difference between this and my previous MRIs was that they used a traceable dye to get a clearer image. The first step for this was the insertion of a cannula (shunt) in my left hand. That hurt, but at least feeling a bit of a prick made a welcome change from feeling a right tit. For a moment, all my bravado and jocularity threatened to desert me as it finally hit me that I was in for some very unpleasant treatment over the next few months. It was quite a moment, a kind of emotional crash. Still, it did not last long, as the pain soon subsided, and the next sight that greeted me was hilarious.

Honestly, the thing you lie on for a breast MRI is the most humour-inducing contraption I have seen since the dog had to wear the cone of shame. Unfortunately, the staff would not let me take a photograph of it from inside the room, as the magnets would have sucked my smartphone into oblivion. A friend told me that she had to have an MRI scan in temporary hospital accommodation and had to change in the same room as the machine. As she removed her bra, the machine's magnetism snatched it out of her clutch and sucked it into its moving parts. The machine was damaged, the MRI postponed. I replied: 'That's funny, though I am sure it was not amusing at the time.' 'Oh yes it was,' she assured me, 'it was bloody hysterical.'

I lay on my front on a table-type thing. It contained a hole that looked like a toilet seat, onto which I rested my head face down. Just south of that were two further holes, into which I dangled my boobs. Yes, really. One hole for each. Each hole was lined with some very comfortable cushioning, but as I was going to be there for around half an hour, I asked for extra cushions and a blanket over my tootsies. I was in the veritable lap of luxury by the time they started.

The first twenty minutes were just fine. The machine made a series of noises so loud that I had been given headphones. It was a cacophony of beeps, buzzes, toots and whirrs – a bit like a hyperactive swarm of bees playing pinball. Every time I swallowed it sounded like an old-fashioned phone ringing in my ears. Very entertaining. So far, so good.

Then they put the dye in through the cannula. They had warned me that I might feel it going in and spreading down my arm. Fine: been there, done that. But as it turned out, the feeling was rather more dramatic. I felt like a pint glass being filled from the bottom up. My abdominal muscles started twitching and I felt woozy and nauseous. I nearly squeezed the squeezy thing that the staff had placed between my fingers in case of problems, but figured I was just being a wuss and that this was perfectly normal.

It turned out that it was not normal, but neither was it particularly problematic. As I stood up when the MRI was all done, I nearly fell over. That is also fine, but I wish I had known it beforehand.

Tumour Humour: Titter Ye Not

They're big and they're flopsy
They had a biopsy

Wore a gown like a nightie
My clothes in the lockers
Some people like me
But I do have my knockers

Tubes in my boobs
Making maps of my baps
Taking bits of my tits
Then I got the answer
It's cancer
Oh shit

Next appointment
They will be pointing
Their surgical pistols
Straight at my Bristols

If I laugh at my thrups
I can cheer myself up
And do what they expect of me:
A successful lumpectomy

My friends are all sending me kisses and hugs
Their very breast wishes to Janine and her jugs

14 October 2016 : Scan Results – One Lump or Two?

The MRI scan result was something of a setback, as it showed a second lump. It was in the same breast, and was pretty small: 4.5mm compared to the 27mm of the 'main' lump, which had already grown since it was last measured. It may not even make much difference, they said – hopefully, they could whip it out during the surgery along with the other lump. But it was not what I wanted to hear, and it brought to mind an image of the cancer spreading.

The most immediate impact of this news was that I had to have more scans. This time, John was with me, which helped very much, especially as this development was unexpected.

Once we got to 'X-Ray 2', it was the gown routine again, with me finally finding out that I had been wearing it the wrong way round on previous visits! The ultrasound was first, so I was prostrate on the table again, with gel on my breast and a radiographer moving the handheld probe over my boob while watching a screen. This second lump was so small that it took lots of moving the device around to finally locate it and take its photo.

Once she had taken a look, the radiographer decided that I needed another biopsy, which I knew from previous experience of a couple of weeks ago was not going to be much fun. So I got John to stand where I could see him without having to see the gigantic needle and the staple gun that would be spending the next ten minutes or so piercing and clicking inside my breast. After taking bits out of my tits, the radiographer then put something in: a metal clip which would help them to find the lump next time they had to go looking for it.

This is an ideal opportunity to discuss distraction techniques. Needles and staple guns are not pleasant, and distracting yourself is a very good idea. Some suggestions:

- Do not get your partner to pull silly faces, especially if your boobs bounce when you laugh. This can make it very hard for the radiographer to aim accurately at a very small lump.
- Recite poems. If you do not write your own, feel free to use mine.
- Before I wrote poems, I used to recite scenes from favourite films during painful medical procedures. I am sure that the staff

will not think you are referring to their hospital as a *wretched hive of scum and villainy*.

• Discuss distraction techniques with the radiographer and nurses while they are carrying out the procedure: a very useful distraction technique in itself.

• Arising from the point above, it appears that two of the most popular are singing and swearing.

• I find that a particularly effective, though somewhat macabre one, is to remind yourself that there are other procedures that are far more painful. I remembered this from childbirth (when I reminded myself that it could be worse, I could be at the dentist) and from going to the dentist (when I reminded myself that it could be worse, it could be childbirth).

• Be assured that the radiographer will not care how eccentric your distraction technique is. S/he just wants you to stay still. Whatever it takes, sisters (and brothers).

The biopsy left a wound, which was sore and covered with a dressing. It would come off a few days later, but until then, there would be no swimming, upper-body exercising or similar exertion. Or going to work.

After the biopsy, I needed a mammogram. It was a repeat performance of my previous one, but with an added bonus: a sideways scan. Just my luck. Sideways mammograms with enormous boobs are hilarious. The table is tilted to vertical, and in the effort to get my breast into the correct position, we ended up with one person crouched under the machine pushing my boob upwards, and the other guiding the transparent plate into place, and me pulling my other boob out of the way. Once in place, the breast was squashed flat between two vertical plates. Feel free to pause and imagine that.

Sadly, your companion is not allowed into the room for the mammogram, so poor John missed out on all of this slapstick entertainment.

Once back in the clinic with the registrar, the other immediate impact of the second lump was revealed: I would not get my surgery date today, but would have to wait another week until the biopsy results came in. I would be discussed at the team meeting next Wednesday then have an appointment on Friday to get the results and, hopefully, set the surgery date and discuss further treatment. Said Friday was my fiftieth birthday. What a way to celebrate. I pitched for a crack-of-dawn appointment as John and I were due to go for a, erm, romantic weekend in a hotel.

I got a bit more information too. (In fact, I think they could have given me this information last time but did not, about which I was a bit peeved.)

• My cancer cells were Grade 2. This was not as bad as Grade 3 (fast-spreading, aggressive), but worse than Grade 1 (slow to grow and spread).
• The cells were oestrogen receptor positive and HER2 receptor negative. This, apparently, was a good combination. It meant that post-surgery, a five-year course of hormone tablets would have a good chance of stopping the cancer coming back.

Before I left the hospital, I collected my prescription charge exemption certificate. When you have cancer, you get free prescriptions for five years, your entitlement proved by a card that slots into your wallet and prevents cash leaving it unnecessarily. It is not that I am tight or anything, but why pay for meds when you don't have to?

Why anyone should have to pay for prescriptions for anything, I do not know. I guess I do know, actually: it is so that pharmaceutical companies can make a lot of money and the government can save a bit of money which it can then give to big companies in tax breaks. What a sick system. How about we scrap prescription charges and bring the pharmaceutical industry into public ownership?

24 October 2016 : Customer Information – Your Treatment Has Been Delayed

I was sitting in an airport writing a blog post. My fiftieth birthday had been on Friday. I had the most excellent of celebrations: a party and book/CD/tour launch the night before; performing with Attila the

Stockbroker and The Men They Couldn't Hang on the big day itself; and a weekend away with John in Lewes. Along the way, I hooked up with some great friends old and new, and paid respects to the victims and survivors of the Aberfan coal disaster, in which 144 lives ended on the day mine began.

When I texted my poem about Aberfan to BBC Radio 5 Live, they rang and asked me to come on air. But I had to say No – because I had to start my birthday with an appointment at the breast cancer clinic.

21 October 1966

A villanelle about the Aberfan coal mining disaster, in which 144 people – including 116 school children – died when a coal mining waste tip collapsed. There was a lot of anger at the National Coal Board for its neglect of safety, and at the inquest one father insisted: 'I want it recorded – Buried alive by the National Coal Board*. That is what I want to see on the record. That is the feeling of those present. Those are the words we want to go on the certificate.'*

The miner insisted the coroner record
The Pantglas School building a homicide scene
They were buried alive by the National Coal Board

His heart was in bits though his shoulders were broad
Though mining was dirty, were consciences clean?
The miner insisted the coroner record

The muck, slush and water had tumbled and poured
The slurry ran black through the valley of green
They were buried alive by the National Coal Board

We all feel this way, the father implored
The mums and the dads of the hundred-sixteen
The miner insisted the coroner record

The standard of care that it did not afford
A tip in a place it should never have been
They were buried alive by the National Coal Board

Aberfan wanted some justice restored
Though justice had perished at 09:13
The miner insisted the coroner record
It was buried alive by the National Coal Board

My disappointment at this was multiplied when it turned out that the appointment was a waste of time. The results of the biopsy on my second lump were not yet in, so the appointment had been rebooked for 1 November. I would not know for another week and a half when my surgery would be or what other treatment I may need.

This was rather frustrating, and not just because I am the world's most impatient outpatient. Aside from my regular job (as a Night Tube station supervisor), I do freelance work running training courses and performing poetry (usually separately, occasionally together). This further delay in setting dates left me with no choice but to cancel a couple of gigs, and feeling guilty about messing about the organisers of gigs and courses. Fortunately they are, to a person, kind and understanding folk.

Over the summer, I had taken a cut in hours – and therefore pay – in my regular job, partly to facilitate more of the freelance work, so this cancer was beginning to impact on my income. In particular, I had just launched my new poetry book/CD/tour, with the expectation of selling the books and CDs on the tour, some of which would now have to be called off. It had a pretty time-specific theme – '16: The Age of Discontent: a ranting, rhyming, revolting review of the year – so possibilities for rebooking were limited. I begged people to help a poet in distress by buying online, and some did. And a few fans took bulk copies and sold them for me. This was very much appreciated.

It did remind me that the regular job is a rock and that all workers deserve reliable employment with decent wages, 100% sick pay and a final-salary pension – and that where we have this, we won it through trade union struggle rather than employer generosity.

Still, the cloudy treatment delay had its silver lining. I could now go ahead with driving to Calais with a convoy of friends, Labour Party activists and donations for the refugees on 2 November. And I could go ahead with my trip to Sofia for a meeting of the European Transport Workers Federation's Women's Committee. That was why I was writing a blog post in an airport: Luton Airport.

II

SURGERY

1 November 2016 : Dates at Last

It was Booby Tuesday again. Today, I would get the result of the biopsy on the second lump and the plan for treatment.

After a fair bit of sitting around in the waiting room, the appointment started with some good news: the second lump is not cancerous, and is probably not even a lump. Hurrah. It seems that MRIs are so powerful that they sometimes detect random little bits of flesh and make them look like horrible little lumps. 'Hang on,' I asked, 'you put a little metal flag in that lump-that-is-not-a-lump-after-all – are you going to dig it out again?' 'No,' came the reply, 'that is yours to keep, it is totally harmless.' Don't say the government never gives you anything for nothing. As I already have titanium in my right eye socket, I was now one tiny step further along the road to becoming a robot.

The less good news was that the treatment itself would be more severe and take longer than I expected. I would have surgery on 14 November and then, after a few weeks of recovery time, three to four weeks of radiotherapy. I could expect to be off work for six months to a year, though I remained hopeful of being able to do lighter work a lot sooner than that. Surgeon Doctor Parvanta explained that for my body, the surgery and subsequent treatment would be rather like a car crash, and I could expect it to be a 'major inconvenience' for around a year.

Surgery day would involve going to a hospital I have never heard of before (the London Independent) to get some radioactive dye injected into my breast, then making my own way to Homerton Hospital for the surgery. Said dye may possibly hang around after the operation and look like a tattoo. I don't have any tats, and have never wanted one, but the prospect of having one on my right breast in the pattern of my blood vessels was quite intriguing.

The surgery would remove the lump and also take out one or more lymph nodes. Although they were pretty sure that the cancer had not spread to the lymph nodes, they wanted to be absolutely certain so would remove a couple to check them. Moreover, removing the nodes that are closest to the breast would close a door to the cancer coming back and spreading in the future. As the surgeon explained, 'I'll remove the ground floor lymph nodes so that the penthouse ones will be safe.'

The surgeon said that the enormous size of my boobs makes her job a lot easier. Actually, I am not sure she used the words 'enormous' or 'boobs', but that was the gist. She offered two options for the surgery, both of which are lumpectomy to my right breast – or, to give them their proper names: wide local excision or segmental mastectomy.

• Option 1 – Remove the lump. My breast would lose some of its size, and the nipple would point downwards. It would not look much different from my viewpoint above, or to the general viewer who sees me with clothes (or a swimsuit) on. It would look significantly different from the front unclothed.

• Option 2 – A surgical lift of the breast as well as the lump removal. The nipple would point in the right direction, but the boob would lose significant size, and I would have further surgery next year to reduce the size of my left breast to match.

Whichever option I chose, there would be no need for breast reconstruction. Shame: I had thought of maybe having a falsie made of mahogany. That would be nice, wooden tit?

I did not have to decide between the two options until the day of the surgery, but I was already leaning heavily towards option 1. I really do not like the idea of surgery on my left breast when there is nothing wrong with it. My breasts have always been a, ahem, very large part of me, and if one of them could come out of this unscathed then that would be great. There is the option (2a?) of doing the surgical lift but not reducing my left breast, but that would leave me with a big one and a little one. I already lean far to the left politically, and have no desire to do so physically as well.

I asked Doctor P which of the two was preferable medically: was one more effective than the other at getting rid of the cancer and preventing it coming back? Reassuringly, she answered that had there been any difference medically, she would not have been offering me a choice.

She told me that it was possible that I may be kept in overnight after the operation, but more likely that they would turf me out on my uppers and send me home for my family to take care of me. Around three weeks after the surgery, I would have a follow-up appointment to look at how my recovery was going and what they had found out from the surgery, and to set the way forward. This may or may not involve chemotherapy, and would definitely involve radiotherapy. That would not be at my local hospital (Homerton), but would necessitate attending Bart's Hospital every weekday for three or four weeks in the run-up to, and possibly during, Christmas. Although it is neither painful nor invasive, radiotherapy would be time-consuming and tiring, and could have various possible side effects.

After all this information, there was a pre-op questionnaire, in which it was quite hard to fit in the answers to 'any previous surgery' in the space provided, and various tests – height, weight, blood pressure (an impressive 108/75) and a blood test. There were also some forms to sign, including permission to store my lump after it has been removed for scientists to poke around in their efforts to better understand cancer (presumably at a future time when we have a government willing to fund such research). I was happy to oblige.

I came away from the hospital pleased that we were progressing, but a little shell-shocked by the prospect of the treatment and its impact. I spent the rest of the day doing two things: cancelling my poetry tour, which made me very sad; and buying and collecting stuff for refugees for my long drive to Calais the next day, which helped me put things in perspective.

*

14 November 2016 : Surgery Day

I had genuinely looked forward to surgery day, and when it arrived, my first stop was the London Independent Hospital in Bethnal Green, a short journey from my home.

For the second time in three months (the previous occasion being surgery on my left ankle), I was having a medical procedure carried out in a private hospital, paid for by the NHS. It is still free at the point of use for me, but I find it very galling. Some part of the fee paid by the NHS to this hospital will end up as profit for its owners. Because of that, it would, by definition, be cheaper for the NHS to provide the procedure itself – unless the private hospital is cutting corners (also known as 'achieving efficiencies') in some way. In 2015-16, the Department of Health paid £8.7 billion to 'independent sector providers', more than double the already-excessive £4.1 billion paid in 2009-10, the year before the Tories came to power with their LibDem junior partners (DoH figures, cited in *The Guardian*, 15 August 2016).

The London Independent is owned by BMI Healthcare, which is owned by the General Healthcare Group (GHG), which is one of the 'big five' operators in the private health market in the UK. It is registered in the British Virgin Islands (corporatewatch.org/news/2012/mar/16/ unhealthy-business-major-healthcare-companies-use-tax-havens-avoid-millions-uk-tax), a group of fifty islands in the Caribbean which charges companies no capital gains tax, gift taxes, sales tax, value added tax, profit tax, inheritance tax or corporation tax. Little wonder that the Islands come highly recommended as a tax haven, with 'beneficial tax arrangements' and 'a high degree of privacy regarding financial transactions' (wis-international.com/british-virgin-islands-tax-haven.html). The company is very keen on making money from the NHS, with its Chief Executive Officer gushing in 2011 that he was 'more excited than ever about what the healthcare marketplace and healthcare reforms mean for the future' and that it would be 'madness not to end up where price became part of the equation' when providing healthcare. The group has performed rather well in the UK, with an EBITDA (Earnings Before Interest, Taxation, Depreciation and Amortisation) of nearly £200m in each of the years 2011 and

2012. But we may as well call that figure EBIDA, as it paid no UK tax in those years. Little wonder that it has close links with the Conservative Party and champions so-called 'NHS reforms' that open up more and more of the National Health Service to private companies to plunder (nhsforsale.info/private-providers/bmi-ghg.html, accessed 23 April 2017).

Anyway, back to Monday morning's business, and my arrival at the aforementioned private hospital. Fortunately, this did not play out like the scene in *The Omen* when devil-spawn Damien's parents take him to church and he shakes and screams so uncontrollably that they have to drive away. I checked in, sat and waited. I appreciated the efforts of the *i* newspaper in providing copies for patients packed with puzzles. These were a useful distraction and brain workout.

I did not have to wait long before I was whisked into the Nuclear Medicine department. I must say that its name above the door was something of a deterrent.

When I had my surgery later that day, back in the arms of the wonderful NHS, the surgeon would need a map of the inside of my breast, and in particular, of my sentinel lymph nodes (the ones that the cancer would be likely to get to first). At least one of these would be removed. Although my cancer had not spread to the lymph nodes, it was apparently a good idea to whip out the nearest ones to the breast to prevent it spreading via this route in future. Hence, the nuclear scan at the London Independent.

The very pleasant radiographer man offered me a female nurse chaperone, but my partner John was with me, so there was no need.

The nuclear scan involves lying on a bed that forms part of a scanning machine, a bit like a mini MRI scanner. The radiographer injected radioactive dye into my breast, just by the nipple. The site of the injection immediately swelled, and I had to massage it to encourage the dye to move along its route towards the lymph nodes. This was rather uncomfortable and stung a bit.

After a bit of massaging, the dye was on its way, and I was on my way into the scanner. Luckily for me, the dye only took a few minutes to complete its journey – for some women, it can take up to half an hour. The scan itself was non-invasive, painless and over quickly. It just involved lying still. Following many years of practice, I am quite good at that.

Having consulted the map of my bap on his screen, the radiographer drew an X on my skin where the sentinel node was, thus becoming the first of three people who would draw on my boob during the course of the day. I felt like an artist's canvas, or perhaps a designer's drawing board – or maybe the walls of a subway attracting an unusual line in cancer-related graffiti.

The radiographer assured me that despite this being a nuclear scan, I was not radioactive. So I cancelled Hug-a-Tory Day and returned home for a brief stopover before the surgery. When I went to the lav, I momentarily forgot having been told that the nuclear dye makes your urine go blue, and thought that a very conscientious member of my family had put some of that lovely blue toilet cleaner in the bowl. Oh no. It was my wee.

After the brief stopover, I went to Homerton Hospital for the actual surgery.

There were five of us booked in for the afternoon surgical stint, and each of us was shown to our own (very) little cubicle. Darn it – if there had been six of us, I would have been able to say, 'That sounds busy, dozen tit?'.

Clothes off, gown on. Visit from the doctor. Questions. Explanations. Letters written on my chest.

- R-WLE: Right Wide Local Excision
- SLNB: SentineL Node Biopsy

Yes, I would be having two operations in one go. The first means removing the cancerous lump and the area around it; the second means removing one or more lymph nodes. Suitably labelled, I now felt reassured that not only would they carry out the correct procedures but that they would carry them out on the correct boob. I took a selfie.

I signed the form donating my tumour to the science geeks so they can use it for research. Hopefully, my lump can play its small (now 2.8mm, having grown a bit more) part in increasing our knowledge of breast cancer, preventing it, detecting it and curing it.

My next visit was from the anaesthetist, who was a very nice man. He asked me the usual list of questions. When I answered that I had had general anaesthetic six times previously, the most recent being less than three months ago, and none with any problems, he seemed most reassured, impressed even. I told him I had a false eye and offered to take it out, but he said there was no need. Nevertheless, he was very pleased that I had told him, as he would now not panic if the pupil of my right eye showed no response.

Then the surgeon, Doctor Parvanta, came, took a good look at my boob and drew on it the lines where she would cut. My breast skin looked a bit like a paper pattern that a dressmaker might use to show where to apply scissors to fabric. Doctor P said that the gigantic size of my breasts made her job a lot easier, which went a little way towards making up for that gigantic size meaning that the cancer had gone unnoticed until it was quite big.

A couple of Kakuros later, it was time for the operation itself and I was wheeled to the prep room. I am one of those people who copes with difficult situations with banter, so I babbled away to the anaesthetists while they popped needles in my hand and adjusted the operating table like a deck chair. I suspected they had finally had enough of my weak jokes and waffling when they put an oxygen mask over my gob.

How had I forgotten how glorious the anaesthetic makes you feel just before it knocks you out? Bloody marvellous.

The next thing I knew, I woke up on the recovery ward, just too late to see the Supermoon through the window. The perigee-syzygy of the Earth-Moon-Sun system, to give it its proper name, is when a full moon or new moon coincides with the Moon coming to the closest point of the Earth on its elliptical orbit. This makes the Moon appear much larger and brighter than usual. On this occasion, it would appear 14% larger and 30% brighter, and the geeky section of the general public – of which I am a lifelong member – was gripped with excitement. Sadly, the notorious British weather conspired to dampen that excitement, as cloud cover meant that everyone else in London missed seeing it too. We will have to wait until 2034 for a full moon to come this close again, and I had the small matter of cancer to beat if I was to be around to see that.

Knowing that the surgery was done, the tea, toast and blackcurrant jam the nurse brought to me tasted lovelier than tea, toast and jam has ever tasted before. The doctor called in to see me and told me that everything had gone swimmingly, and after a check of my vital signs, I was given a pack of painkillers and leaflets, led downstairs to a taxi by John, and was home in time for *Home and Away*.

Lucky Me

What a lucky fucker am I
that when that firework hit my eye
I didn't die

And who even knew
that although you're better off with two
that just one eye will do
just fine, you see
Lucky, lucky me

And when I got a killer disease
I got the sort they can cure with ease
if you please

Surgery
Urgently
Blackcurrant jam on toast with tea
Lucky, lucky me

21 November 2016 : Post-Op Week 1

Back home from the hospital on the very (Mon)day that I had the operation, I felt remarkably cheery and pain-free. Obviously the anaesthetic had not yet fully worn off.

The huge support from friends and family also kept my mood upbeat. I could not possibly reply to each individually, but I hoped that through my blog and social media, people knew that each and every one gave me a boost and was (and still is) very much appreciated. Also much appreciated were the various cards, flowers and the Lego White House set (thanks Ronne!). I planned to build it and install it with a minifig resident much more capable and compassionate than the real-life recently-elected inhabitant.

The hospital had armed me with co-codamol and naproxen, and between them, they pretty much kept the pain at bay. They also (specifically the co-codamol) kept the smooth running of my bowels at bay. Be warned: C-CCC – co-codamol causes constipation. Invest in a lot of oranges and/or prunes and a good book.

On Wednesday, I managed to deliver a lecture, by pre-recorded video. Every year, the George Lansbury Memorial Lecture sees a well-known expert deliver a talk on an aspect of Good Old George's life – until this year, when it was me! It was over a year since I had been invited to give a lecture on George Lansbury, Minnie Lansbury and their relevance to modern feminism. I had happily accepted, as Minnie is my political hero and I have a personal mission to spread knowledge of this suffragette, school teacher, champion of war orphans, communist and rebel councillor who packed a whole lot of necessary trouble-making into her tragically short 32 years. When I had found out the surgery date a couple of weeks previously, I realised that I would not be able to give the lecture in person, and when a few efforts to arrange a substitute proved impractical, I spent the evening before the operation sitting on my sofa with my son Alex's MacBook and recorded it instead. Alex and I added some pictures post-op, again in the living room. On lecture day itself, my dad (David) and a friend (Peter) came round, which was fabulous though tiring, and which enabled my other 'arf John and my son Joe to go to the lecture. Another forty-odd people went too (meaning approximately forty people rather than forty people who are odd), and apparently all went very well. Should you be so inclined, you can watch the lecture on my website or my YouTube channel or read it in a pamphlet.

Thursday was a day of rest and of continuing attempts to work out how to wash effectively whilst not wetting or disturbing the wounds.

This, I can confirm, is tricky.

On Friday, I had to go to the GP's surgery for the nurse to change my dressings. That was when I saw it. When the nurse removed the dressings, there was the wound in its full glory: over a foot long, stitched along its length from the bottom corner of my right breast all the way to the nipple and all the way round it. It had been dressed in one of those spongy dressings with holes in it, so it was now covered with raised circles of flesh. It was awash with every shade of yellow, blue, brown, purple and red you could imagine: the full range of bruisey hues.

The other 'arf had come along to support and help me, and his face was a picture. I thought he was going to freeze and keel over like Neville Longbottom when Hermione Grainger did *Petrificus Totalis* on him. I managed to bring him back to consciousness in time to take some photos. There was also a six-inch wound under my armpit and a slightly infected sore patch of skin that would need some TLC.

Four days on from the operation, the visit to the GP's surgery had been my first trip out of the house. It was a refreshing experience to walk a couple of kilometres, and I felt perky enough to have another friend (Yvonne) come round, and to write a union leaflet.

I had more rest over the weekend, and on Sunday a visit from my secret photographer friend Natasha. She was photographing me at various stages of the treatment to maintain a photolog of the changes to my body. Whether, when and how these will be published remained to be decided.

I was not yet fit enough to help with the Labour Party's campaign day to defend the National Health Service, which took place on Saturday 26 November. So I contributed by writing a poem.

It's Not Me, It's You

It isn't my humour
That sees off my tumour
Or my banter and mocking derision

It isn't my laugh
But the medical staff
And their caring, their skills, their precision

Being mouthy and tough
Just isn't enough
To see off the murderous cells
Brashness and bragging
Coolness and swaggering
Do no better than snake oil or gels

Yes, a fighter am I
And will be till I die
Not just to the lump in my breast
I will be to my death
To my last, final breath
A defender of our NHS

1 December 2016 : Bored Now – Post-Op Weeks 2 and 3

The novelty had worn off by the second week after surgery, and sitting round recovering was beginning to get on my tits.

The big, long wound was healing steadily but very slowly. The other wound, under my armpit, had a stubborn sore patch next to it. Eight days after the surgery, I had another walk to the GP's surgery to have the dressings changed again, and to get some advice on what to do.

I was experiencing some difficulty with the BBC – the Big Boob Conundrum. The surgical wounds would benefit from exposure to air, but the boob's weight strained them without the support of a bra. So, the BBC compromise is to be topless – or at least braless – when resting at home, but to don the over-shoulder-boulder-holder (a term recovered from my memory of my teenage years) when I am up and about.

*

BBC: Big Breast Cancer

Big breast cancer:
Basically, biologically, clinically
Bog-standard breast cancer
But brings complications

Bad bastard cells
Build big clumps
Burrowed, buried, concealed
Beneath buxom cover
Before being caught

Biopsy bores centimetres
Beyond B cups
Big bloody clippers
Biting bosom cancer

Bras brush, catch
Bouncy boobs cannot
Bear burdensome cuts
Broken bruises colonise
Bad bacterial cultures

But bigguns can
Be beneficial cases
Because broader choices
Benefit better cutting

Best, beat, cure
Big breast cancer

I managed to get out to the doctor and to the post office a couple of times, and – best of all – to watch my youngest son Harrison perform the role of Johnny Casino in his school production of *Grease*. He, and all his schoolmates, were just brilliant. There was such an array of talent on show, and their hard work over the last six months really showed in their acting, songs and dance routines. I could not get the songs out of my head, and the joke about the jugs certainly had me tittering. In contrast with the film, we had a very multi-racial Hackney working-class student body playing the parts of the '50s American high school students. It was one of those nights that made me feel glad to be alive.

I hit something of a low point one evening soon after, heartily sick of wanting to do things and not being able to. The spirit was willing but the body weak, so the spirit got weak too. I expected that I would steadily feel better after the operation, but it did not work out that way. Some days I felt worse than the day before: partly because as the wounds heal, the feeling returns and the feeling is pain; partly because I was not getting exercise so I felt like I was withering.

The support of friends and family continued to prove invaluable, with particular thanks due to Terry and Marie for coming round during these difficult days, bearing, respectively, plants and a Lego *Stars Wars* advent calendar. It was great to see my mum and dad too.

2 December 2016 : Results and Prospects

This was the day when I would be told how well or otherwise the surgery had gone, and it turned out to be a good news day. The surgeon told me that:

• They got it all out – the tumour and all surrounding areas are gone, departed, no more, not pining for the fjords etc.; I would not need any more surgery.

• There is no cancer in the lymph nodes, not a bit, a trace or a smidgeon.

Treatment from here on would be about preventing it coming back, and there followed the less good news: the examination of the factors influencing whether I need chemotherapy (e.g. the aggressiveness of the cancer) had proved inconclusive. Some factors suggest I would benefit from it, some not. So, further testing was required. Fortunately, this testing was not of me but of the tumour they removed from me.

I had a few questions and got a few answers. One of these was: Will I ever get the feeling back in my nipple? The answer was that we would know that in about a year's time.

From this point, my care was transferred to the oncologists based at Bart's Hospital, whom I would meet within the next two weeks. Farewell, surgeon Doctor Parvanta – you were brilliant. In the meantime, the radiotherapy was on hold, because although I would definitely need to have it, if I needed chemo as well, that would need to be done first. Unlike the turkeys, I would not be microwaved (or stuffed) over Christmas.

My wounds were continuing to heal quite well, but given their size and severity, this was still a long and rather painful process, made longer and more painful by the weight of my breast. More dressings were removed and applied, and the new ones would be checked and reapplied the following Tuesday.

The major frustration with all this was not knowing what was going to happen when. The timing was rather unfortunate for me, as you will remember that I had recently cut my hours in my regular job (which has 100% sick pay) in order to do more freelance work training and performing (which has 0% sick pay). I hated not being able to guarantee when I would be available for this work. I felt that I was letting people down. Still, I had no choice but to crack on as best I could and take the opportunity to do some writing. As I mentioned, I am a very impatient patient.

I got some leaflets and information about wellbeing and exercise, and resolved to apply myself to that from the following week. Having received lots of messages cheering me on in my fight against cancer, there was something in particular that I wanted to write about.

Am I Fighting Cancer? Yes, But ...

'Fighting cancer' is a term often said, but also a matter of some discomfort and debate. I had been pummelling the philosophical punchbag of the issues, and was ready to set out my thoughts.

Yes, I was fighting cancer. It is a battle, and if you survive, you get bloodied and bruised and can come out injured, physically and psychologically. You get knocked down, you get up again. And like a fighter, I was spending a lot of my time stripped to the waist being attended to by medics.

Some people say that the term 'fighting cancer' is too aggressive. But I did not go looking for this fight. Cancer started it. If I was fighting cancer, then it was only because cancer picked a fight with me. I plead self-defence.

In any case, what are the alternative terms to 'I'm fighting cancer'? I 'have cancer'? Sorry to be pedantic, but that was not true at every point. I had cancer, surgery removed it, and now I was waging an intense counter-insurgency campaign to stop it coming back. I was 'living with cancer'? That sounds too cosy and domestic, although obviously preferable to dying from cancer.

But what about when people say 'you will beat cancer because you're a fighter'? It is said with good intentions, but it is a problem.

We do not wave soldiers off to war saying, 'You'll survive, you're a fighter'. Why not? Because we know very well that some will die and some will live and that which side the tossed coin falls for each soldier depends very little on how much of, or how good, a fighter she or he is. It depends a good deal more on luck, and on the balance of forces between 'our' side and the enemy.

So it is with cancer too. Survival depends on the type and grade of the cancer, the part of the body affected, the stage at which it was discovered, and your access to treatment (e.g. whether the country you live in has a free public health service). Many very brave people have fought cancer as hard as it is possible to fight it, but have still lost. They did not lose because they did not fight, but because cancer won. I saw two good friends of mine, thirteen years apart, fight tooth and nail against the aggressive forms of cancer that finally killed them, both at the age of 45, both having raised money and sought out experimental treatments when the conventional, approved ones failed. Both Rob and Brian showed enormous humour, strength of character, determination and optimism. They were fighters, but they lost.

Was I fighting cancer? Yes, I was. But it was not my belligerent attitude that would (or would not) defeat cancer: it was medicine.

Nurses, surgeons, radiographers, radiotherapists, oncologists, cleaners, receptionists, pharmacists, caterers, porters, anaesthetists, researchers, dieticians, therapists, physios and more are the army that is fighting cancer. All I had to do was co-operate with them.

And defend them. This is the fight that is the most important assault on cancer: the fight to defend our National Health Service from private parasites and Tory cutters. By joining this crucial struggle, we can all be fighting cancer, whether or not each of us is fighting a cancer inside us.

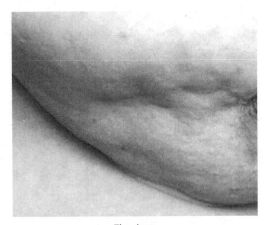

The dent.
[Photo: © Natansky.co.uk]

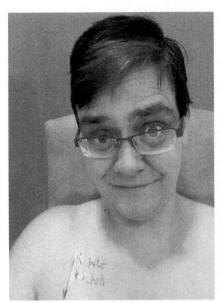

Arts and Crafts day.
Ensuring they operate
on the right one.

[Photos courtesy of the author]

III

BETWEEN TREATMENTS

2 December 2016 : At the Hospital

The hospital volunteers were serving free tea and coffee today. Four older folks sitting on the row of chairs along from me looked like they'd love a nice cuppa but might struggle walking round the corner to the main waiting room to get it, so I offered and they ordered. Two wanted coffee, both with milk, one with sugar. The third wanted nothing thanks, love. The fourth opened his hand and unclasped a coin. He wanted to give a pound. People are lovely, aren't they?

Cups full delivered, I took to passing time drinking my choice of hot beverage from the volunteers' trolley and listening to the chat around me.

Waiting

'It's cheap coffee, this,
And I can't taste the sugar.'
'Well I saw her put it in.
I brought a jar of nice
coffee with me just
in case you get admitted.'
'What did you do that for?'
'I just thought you'd like it.'
'Oh.'
'How many in front of us now?'
'Three, I think, or four.

Really, I'm not sure.'
'Is anyone in that toilet?'
'Don't know. You can't
tell, but I've not seen
anyone going in.'
'We've been waiting
longer than him.'

'At least the seats are softer
And it's warmer than
the doctor's.
Mustn't grumble.'

'You'll want a decent cup
of coffee after this.'

14 December 2016 : Infection Dejection

When you have a 15-inch surgical wound, there is a fair chance that an inch or two of it will become infected. When it does, it will be horrid, painful, smelly, leave a worse scar and – more worryingly – may delay the treatment needed to keep the cancer from coming back.

While the wound under my armpit was healing slowly but surely, and most of the longer wound was gradually healing too, part of the wound around my nipple had become infected. As well as keeping it clean, I now had to go to hospital every Tuesday and Thursday to have it checked and the dressings changed, and had to start a two-week course of antibiotics. No Christmas sherry for me!

As well as the new tablets, the infection meant keeping up the painkillers. The combination of medication and enforced immobility became pretty debilitating. It was difficult to balance the need to rest with the need to get at least *some* fresh air and exercise. And while it was lovely that so many friends showed their concern for me, repeatedly telling someone as driven as I am that I must rest is a bit like telling a depressed person to cheer up or an over-excited person to calm down. It does not work too well.

I was supposed to be seeing the oncologist on Thursday or Friday of this particular week, but despite several enquiries, they would not give me the date and time until the Thursday morning. Thus far, I had not mentioned to the cancer staff that I am autistic (although it is of course in my medical records) because thus far, it had not been an issue. But this uncertainty about appointment times was in danger of making it an issue.

15 December 2016 : A Communication Cock-Up and a Transatlantic Trip

Having still received no appointment news, I chased again, and was told that it will be in the new year. An hour later, I got a letter through the post stating that my appointment would be on 29 December!

This poor communication was a nuisance. Even cancer patients have to plan our lives, and I had family responsibilities and freelance work that I had to fit around my treatment. I did not want to overstate or make a big deal about this, and I certainly did not blame the hard-pressed, over-stretched NHS staff. Years of government (Tory and previously 'New' Labour) ranting against 'bureaucracy' in the health service had led to major cuts in genuinely-needed administration. So you inevitably get a major case of left-hand-right-hand syndrome.

I was more concerned about the delay to my treatment. After a cancerous tumour is removed by surgery, you need treatment to stop it coming back, and this should start within four to six weeks (according to the hospital) or 31 days (according to the pamphlet that the hospital gave me). Whatever happened at my appointment, 29 December was past this time window.

Why the delay? Because they had to send my tumour tissue to the USA. I needed to have an Oncotype DX test – a relatively new test which looks at gene activity to assess whether chemo would have much impact – which is done in America. I quite fancied a trip to the USA, but it would be my tumour that got to go, not me. Shame. I hoped that Donald Trump would let it in once it arrived.

What I really wanted to know was … Why can't this country test cancer samples itself rather than delaying treatment? And how much does this transatlantic treatment cost the NHS compared with doing it here? A generation of governments starving the NHS and making it farm out various of its functions means that many things are now done by outside organisations (usually for profit). But outsourcing across the Atlantic? That's a new one on me. I resolved to investigate.

24 December 2016 : Christmas with Cancer

Actually, I was spending Christmas with my family. Cancer, the uninvited guest, had been banished, and the new year would begin with essential work to stop it coming back.

For most of December, I had been going to Homerton Hospital twice a week to have my surgical wound checked and dressings changed. Iodine gauzes, big comfy dressings, antibiotics and supportive bras had between them seen off the wound infection. There were some irritating patches of sore skin, as the adhesive on the dressing was very sticky and tended to take a layer of skin with it every time the dressing was removed. Because of this, each new dressing was put on in a slightly different position to the previous one.

The rest of the wound had healed very well, the swelling had reduced, and I was beginning to get a feel of what my breast would be like post-cancer.

Christmas dinner number one was on Christmas Eve Eve (23 December), cooked most expertly by my youngest son, twelve-year-old Harrison, with a little help from his dad. Christmas dinner number two was on the day itself, at my parents' house, with John's parents joining us for the day. The internet, together with a local bookshop and gallery, had made present-buying fairly straightforward despite limited mobility.

I wished huge seasonal solidarity to those having a rougher time with cancer than I was this Christmas, and to the NHS staff who had been looking after me. I would usually be working at this time of year, so have some idea of what it is like to serve the revellers rather than being one of them. Indeed, health workers and London Underground workers serve some of the same people: those who over-consume and come a-cropper on the train or the escalators or elsewhere and find themselves travelling in an ambulance to Accident and Emergency instead of on the Victoria Line to that party. Luckily for the breast clinic nurses, they did not have to work over Christmas itself, but they would be back at it a couple of days later.

And so would I, seeing the oncologist a few days after Christmas to find out whether I would be spending January being poisoned with chemotherapy or microwaved with radiotherapy.

Battle Scars

Penicillin
is killing
the infection.
Inspection
revealed
it's healed.
I brandish
the bandage
removed
from the wound.
My breast
undressed.

29 December 2016 : Result!

Finally, my results were back, and at an appointment at Bart's Hospital this morning, the oncologist set out my treatment plan. My joke of the day was that my breast tumour had been sent to the USA, where tests revealed it to be an aggressive piece of tissue that attacks women: so Donald Trump had appointed it to his Cabinet.

The good news was that I did not need chemotherapy. The idea of months of feeling rubbish and running to the loo to vomit several times a day did not fill me with excitement. So, no yodelling down the great white canyon for me. Hurrah.

Here is how the Stateside test worked. It checks out the activity of various genes in your cancer cells, which determines how responsive you will be to chemo. So from a certain point of view, my test result was not good news after all: it showed that chemotherapy would not work to stop my cancer coming back. But I chose to see it as good news, that I had dodged the puking agonies of fighting cancer by throwing poison at it.

The Oncotype DX test is used to assess invasive ductal breast cancer (the sort that is in the milk ducts – as against the nodules – and has the potential to spread) which is oestrogen-receptor positive and HER-receptor negative. That was the type of cancer I had, as revealed by the biopsy taken at the start of this journey.

The test's results fall into three bands: high (chemo will have significant benefit in preventing the cancer returning), intermediate (some benefit) and low (negligible benefit). My result was low (14/100). High would have meant having chemotherapy, and intermediate would have been even more difficult – I would have had to make a decision! On some days, picking between tea and coffee is hard enough: a potentially life-and-death choice would have driven my brain into such overdrive that you would probably have been able to hear the whirring several hundred miles away.

I would now have two treatments to help prevent the cancer returning:

• Tamoxifen tablets – one a day for ten years, although this will be reviewed, and perhaps changed, after five years (the prescription charge exemption will certainly come in handy). I was pleased that the oncologist was planning this far ahead, as it suggested that she expected me to still be alive.

• Radiotherapy – three or four weeks visiting Bart's Hospital every weekday for a machine to blast with radiation the area where my tumour was. This would probably start in January, but I would have an appointment with the oncological radiologist first.

Tamoxifen is a small, tasteless, 20mg pill which can be taken with or without food, at the same time every day. I decided to take it when I got up in the morning, although if I have side effects, I could switch this to the evening. I popped my first one at the bus stop on the way home from hospital. The medication would block the effect of oestrogen on the receptors, and so help to stop any breast cancer cells from growing. That means that it would significantly reduce the chance of the cancer coming back after surgery. This is known as adjuvant therapy.

There are some other situations in which Tamoxifen may be used against breast cancer: when the cancer returns locally; for secondary breast cancer; as a preventative treatment for women with a significant family history of breast cancer; and occasionally as the first treatment, before or instead of surgery.

Tamoxifen has a fairly long and slightly scary list of possible side effects, including hot flushes, night sweats, changes to periods, mood swings, bone thinning, nausea – even, albeit rarely, uterine cancer, which would surely be the cancer equivalent of being surgically removed from the frying pan and medicated into the fire.

Radiotherapy has a similarly long and frightening list, headed by skin effects, tiredness, pain, fluid retention, local hair loss and making your ribs brittle.

I resolved to cross these bridges if and when I came to them.

Before leaving the hospital, I had blood tests taken, mainly to establish whether I had been through the menopause or not. Strange question, you may think, expecting quite reasonably that I would know that already. But as I had an intra-uterine device fitted, I did not have periods (which is why I had an intra-uterine device!) so I did not know. And as I had forgotten exactly what sort of IUD I had, I needed to find the paperwork that came with it or phone the clinic that fitted it. Where I am with the menopause makes a difference to the effect that the treatments will have on me, and whether the Tamoxifen should at some point be switched to a different hormone treatment.

The conclusion of this appointment was that I was not out of the woods yet, but the cancer had gone and an arsenal of pills and microwaves was going to stop it coming back. And even if that knocked me over for a while, all in all it was going to be a happy new year.

The Price of Progress : Capitalism and Cancer

Radiotherapy is supposed to start within six weeks of surgery; mine eventually started twelve weeks after. Only time would reveal the impact of this delay, but it could mean that my cancer comes back when it would not have done so otherwise.

Why did the tumour have to be posted half way round the world? The Oncotype DX test was developed and is run by a private company in the USA called Genomic Health. The UK's National Health Service has been using it since approving it in 2013 and has to pay for each test, at around £2,500 a go (breastcancercare.org.uk/oncotype-dx). In countries without a public health service like ours, individuals have to pay this fee, either straight from their pocket or via their insurance premiums. Or they do not have the test, in which case they either have unnecessary chemo, or they do not have chemo because they cannot afford that either, hoping but not knowing that it would make no difference to the likelihood of their cancer coming back. From this ready market of the sick and afraid, Genomic Health's 2016 revenues topped three hundred million dollars (fool.com/investing/general/2016/02/08/the-one-question-for-genomic-health-inc.aspx).

Perhaps ironically, one of the benefits of the test is to prevent unnecessary treatment. In the USA, there is genuine concern about cancer being 'over-treated'. In the UK, we would probably like to see more screening for breast cancer: for example, starting regular mammograms at a younger age than fifty. But in the USA, the worry is the opposite: that women may be pressured into having more mammograms than necessary, to an extent that may even be harmful.

The difference between the two countries? In the USA, healthcare is a private market, where profit-making companies compete to pressure frightened patients into buying their products – whether medications or mammograms – and where the treatment you get depends on the content of your bank account. In the UK, we have a public National Health Service, which aims to provide treatments on the basis of need, but which receives inadequate funding from the government and shells out a portion of that to private companies such as Genomic Health.

Decisions on which treatments the NHS may buy from private companies fall to the National Institute for Health and Care Excellence (NICE), which is caught between the rock of insufficient funds and the hard place of profiteers' demands. In December 2016, NICE declined a medication called Kadcyla (theguardian.com/society/2016/dec/29/breast-cancer-drug-kadcyla-rejected-for-nhs-use-on-cost-benefit-grounds), which prolongs the life of women with advanced breast cancer but which, at £90,000 per patient per year, was reckoned to be too expensive for the benefits it provides. Kadcyla is produced by Roche Pharmaceuticals, which made a core operating profit of 18.4 billion Swiss Francs (about £14.5 billion) in 2016 (roche.com/investors/ar16e_performance.html #overview).

These private companies are fully within their legal rights to refuse to share their medical breakthroughs with cancer treatment practitioners around the world, and instead to charge a fortune or to insist that every tumour to be tested is sent to California along with the fee, while patients wait impatiently.

The companies' profiteering is not just lawful, it is the basic way in which capitalism operates. Capitalists own the means of production privately, and utilise them and workers' labour to produce products that they can sell at a profit. Capitalism thus provides a drive to develop new technologies, tests and treatments, and so has brought massive leaps forward in healthcare. But it also puts a hefty price-tag on them and reduces their effectiveness by building division and delay into the process.

Individual companies' research departments are doubtless working very hard to develop new treatments – even cures – for cancer. After all, a crock of profit awaits the business that strikes cancer-cure gold. But imagine if, rather than thousands of different companies' laboratories carrying out separate, secret, similar research, they all worked together, pooling knowledge and planning their investigations, collaborating in search not of riches but of alleviating human suffering. What if a new test was developed and laboratories all over the world were allowed to use it? What if life-extending medications were made available to patients on the basis of need not cost? That would be good, wouldn't it?

1 January 2017 : Bleurgh Humbug

In my 20s, I would have spent most of New Year's Day in bed because I didn't go to bed until the Day was well under way. A little later, a hangover might have kept me in bed all day. Then with the advent of kids, no days could be spent in bed, least of all New Year's. Now I had turned fifty, New Year's Day was spent largely in bed dealing with cancer treatment side effects.

The Tamoxifen had kicked in, keeping the cancer from returning but bringing with it headaches, dizziness, all-over aching, that pukey feeling, and chain-yawning tiredness. I could not help but crawl under the duvet after lunch and stay there until dinner.

Over the last couple of days, I had received three letters from the hospital (by 'the hospital', I now mean Bart's rather than Homerton, as my care had transferred post-surgery). The first told me that my appointment with the radiotherapy team was on Friday 27 January. Oh, I thought, I had expected it to be sooner than that. I was not sure what to make of that, but my impatient patient syndrome was getting jumpy. I chose to believe that the four-week wait was because they had no grounds for urgency and not because of lack of resources.

Then I got another two letters inviting me to appointments with the oncologist on Thursday 6 and Monday 16 January. It was not that I had been expecting these earlier or later: I had not been expecting them at all. I Hmmmed another, slightly longer and more puzzled, Hmmm. Perhaps something had come up on my blood tests.

I was glad, though – if the side effects I was experiencing continued, then a session with the onco was just what the doctor ordered.

5 January 2017 : You'll SHARE if you CARE

Five days into the new year, little hearts began to appear on Facebook walls. No message, no explanation, just a heart. Apparently this would help the fight against breast cancer. Some undoubtedly well-meaning friends messaged me (and probably all their other friends) asking me to post said heart.

I was already mightily naffed off with social media contacts who posted status updates along the lines that anyone who does not copy and paste said status update does not care about cancer victims, animals, disabled children, soldiers etc. Posting, or reposting, or sharing this stuff does not help tackle the actual issue one bit. It may make you feel better, or you may think it makes others think you are a caring person, but it moves no molehills, let alone mountains.

Rather than a heart, share an advert for an NHS demonstration, copy and paste advice on checking your boobs, send a message to a friend who is facing the Big C, or drop an email to your MP expressing your concern about the denial of cutting-edge cancer treatments to patients who need them on the grounds of cost. Or get off the keyboard and get involved in your local NHS campaign group, or phone that pal you have been meaning to phone and offer to accompany him or her to their next chemo session.

Sadly, I felt entitled to vent about the pointless hearts only because I was battling cancer myself. If I were not, then I would expect complaints of 'You don't understand', 'You don't know how it feels', 'That post really means a lot to some people', 'How very dare you?' and so on. But I was, so I could.

I considered taking up a friend's suggestion and posting a breast on my timeline to fight heart disease, though it would probably have breached Facebook's community standards.

Having sounded off, I went to my appointment at Bart's. It turned out that it had been randomly generated by the hospital's admin system and was not really necessary. Looking on the bright side, though, I came away armed with more test results (I am pre-menopausal), some pamphlets, a three-month sick note and an invitation to a free massage whenever I want one. Result.

23 January 2017 : Clickbait and Miracle Cures

Another day, another headline, another cure for or cause of cancer. On 23 January, it was the claim that brown toast causes cancer. On another day, it might have been that turmeric prevents it. Thousands of people affected by cancer click these links, wanting to read some rare good news, wanting to gain at least a little control over their or their loved one's fate.

Knowledge is power, and of course anyone facing a life-threatening illness – and anyone interested in human progress – wants to read about new insights, new discoveries, new hope. With the pharmaceutical industry driven by marketing-for-profit, it is little surprise that people do not necessarily trust the medical establishment and want to look at other options.

Some of the reports are informative and useful, and it is a good idea to seek out a balanced and scientific assessment. But sadly, many reports are exaggerated, flimsy and tenuous, fronted up by headlines that function as clickbait.

Well-meaning friends regularly messaged me tips about cancer-fighting foods. It was thoughtful of them, and I politely thanked them (well, as politely as my notorious autistic bluntness allows). But here's the thing: healthy eating is healthy eating, cancer or no cancer. Cut down sugars, eat fruit and veg, keep up your vitamins. Turmeric and spinach taste delicious as well as being packed with the good stuff. Eating the superfoods is good nutritional practice, but *it is not a cure for cancer*.

Well-meaning becomes dangerous with claims that diet alone can cure cancer – not as a supplement to surgery and adjuvant therapy, but as an alternative. Take David Wolfe (please), a man who has made himself a social media profile with warm-hearted inspiration-porn memes, but also tries to persuade cancer patients to refuse surgery and other medical treatments and rely instead on raw foods. He is a pseudo-scientist who spreads quackery to vulnerable people. Little wonder that social media campaign #DontCryWolfe urges people not to share his material online (forbes.com/sites/kavinsenapathy/2016/01/01/a-new-years-resolution-for-science-advocates-dont-cry-wolfe/#3e17340511fd).

Along with the likes of Wolfe, we hear the continual heckle of magic beans and miracle cures that are just *not*. The QuackWatch website lists over 120 dubious treatments for cancer, each of which has claimed effectiveness in curing or slowing the disease but without credible scientific evidence. There are those named to sound like proper medicines – such as Antimalignocyt (CH-23), Antineoplastons and Gc-MAF (also called GcMAF) – and those which attribute life-saving powers to vitamin C, shark cartilage and wheatgrass.

Claims of miracle cures for cancer – usually with a price tag – are nothing new. In April 1914, Harry Delvine was convicted of obtaining money by false pretences. He had charged cancer sufferers for treatment with herbal liquids, showing them pigs' entrails and claiming they were the tumour he had removed (*Daily Herald*, 27 March, 11 April and 29 April 1914).

By the 1930s, there was such a proliferation of quack cancer cures that Parliament passed the 1939 Cancer Act. Although the Act has been revised several times since, with many sections repealed, the section that bans the advertising of cancer treatments and cures to the public is still in force – and it is still used. Trading Standards authorities regularly bring prosecutions, recently against people who have claimed that colloidal silver can cure cancer (*Chelmsford Weekly News*, 15 September 2014), maintained that protein shakes and vitamin supplements had cured two patients (MailOnline, 6 May 2014), and offered distance healing to cure cancer (*Worcester News*, 12 March 2010).

Prosecutors have charged not only cranky individuals but also 'legitimate' private healthcare companies. In 2009, private company Healthwize UK was fined £2,000 for advertising Ellegic Acid, claiming that it could inhibit the growth of cancer cells (*Nottingham Post*, 9 March 2009). While many people believe that the private healthcare industry suppresses alternative treatments, at least some private companies seem to have spotted an opportunity to make money from people who are attracted to them.

If your friends tell you that turmeric will cure your cancer, try asking them why the manufacturers and retailers of turmeric do not make this claim. It is because they would be prosecuted – if not under the Cancer Act, then under the Consumer Protection from Unfair Trading Regulations 2008, which prohibit 'falsely claiming that a product is able to cure illness'.

In the meantime, I continued to do what the medics were telling me to.

Brown Toast

Brown toast causes cancer
Quinoa shrinks your dick
Ketchup makes you retch
And Tories make you sick

26 January 2017 : One Thing After Another

You will recall that I had attended a fictitious appointment but had tried to made the best of it by bringing home plenty of printed information. Reading one of the pamphlets – on food and drink during cancer treatment – I had discovered that moderate alcohol intake was fine, and concluded I had not been consuming enough. As an obedient and sensible patient, I resolved to address this shortcoming.

The tiredness, dizziness and headaches that had begun a week after starting Tamoxifen continued unabated. I ended up phoning the cancer nurses, who got back to me saying that the doctors wanted me to have a brain scan. But of course, no sooner had I phoned up moaning about my side effects than said side effects abated!

You will also recall that I had to check what sort of intra-uterine device I had. The answer was a Mirena coil: a small, anchor-shaped contraption that releases very small doses of contraceptive directly into the uterus wall and avoids the unpleasant side effects of other IUDs. I have had heavy and painful (to put it mildly) periods all my life, and the Mirena coil put a stop to them. But my blessed relief would soon have to come to an end. As my cancer is hormone-driven, and the Tamoxifen tablets I am taking to stop the cancer returning are hormonal, then I cannot continue having a hormone-based device.

So a few days later, I went to the Ivy Centre at St. Leonard's Hospital, the sexual health clinic that fitted the coil, to have it removed. It was a pretty straightforward procedure, rather like having a cervical smear test: not painful, but a bit uncomfortable, and if you are embarrassed by this sort of thing (which I am thankfully not), a bit embarrassing.

Annoyingly, while removing the coil, the nurse saw something a bit dodgy-looking, and advised me to see a gynaecologist. To do that, I would have to go to my GP and get a referral. It was beginning to feel like dealing with cancer was just one thing after another.

I was back at Bart's on 23 January for an appointment to set up my radiotherapy. After the explanation and a repeat of the faintly-concerning list of possible side effects, I signed the consent forms. The oncologist told me that, starting on a date I would be told shortly (but likely to be around 6 February), I would attend the hospital every weekday for four weeks to be zapped. The pamphlet said three weeks, I asked why is it four for me? 'Because you are young,' he said. Bless. Having cancer at fifty means that I am young.

I called in at the hospital again a few days later to pick up my Tamoxifen prescription, on a particularly freezingly cold day. I used to get nasty pain in both my nipples during cold weather. Following breast cancer surgery, I now got it in only one of them. Silver lining, eh? Or, perhaps, a 42J cup half full.

A triptych of hospitals.
From top: The London Independent; Homerton; St. Bartholomew's.
[Photos courtesy of the author]

IV

RADIOTHERAPY

1 February 2017 : Measuring Up to be Microwaved

As February began, I was off to my radiotherapy booking appointment in the basement of Bart's Hospital.

I filled forms, signed consents, stripped and gowned. I shared the waiting area with a hairless woman and her two kids, a young adult daughter and a teenage-ish son. She was having radiotherapy to her brain. I pondered on my good fortune.

Then I was taken to the radiotherapy room, past a door marked 'Mould Room': I resolved to stay out of there.

My team of three radiotherapists were all friendly, kind and chatty. When I mentioned that I am a poet, they asked for an ode, and the one that came to mind was a limerick about then Health Secretary Jeremy Hunt. I will leave it to you to imagine what rhyme I used. You can't go wrong having a go at Jeremy Hunt to NHS staff: hardly surprising, given his and the Tory government's relentless attacks on the health service and its staff's working conditions. My joke about sending my tumour to the USA went down well too. 'We've got a comedian here,' they advised (or warned) colleagues.

As instructed, I lay on my back with my hands interlaced above my head. The size of my breasts prompted intense discussion among the team, with the oncologist and the guy from the aforementioned Mould Room joining the deliberations. This is when I found out that the Mould Room was where they make special moulds, usually to protect your face when having radiotherapy to the eyes, brain or other head parts, but occasionally to prop up massive knockers. It sounded rather more pleasant than the mouldy room that I had imagined.

The assembled experts tilted their heads, nibbled their pens, furrowed their brows, and contemplated the way that my breast rested. Eventually, they decided that my boobs lie so beautifully that I would not need a mould. This was simultaneously reassuring and disappointing, as I had already secured their agreement that I could keep the mould after the treatment. Ah well.

Discussion concluded, we moved on to the scan. It was a similar experience to the MRI scan, but much briefer and without the horrid drippy thing. All I had to do was to lie back and relax as my body moved in and out of a large whirring drum. All good.

Once it was over, I opened my eyes and looked down, to see a green laser-type line of light straight up the middle of my body. My mind was invaded by that scene in *Goldfinger*. But the line of light simply indicated that I was lying perfectly symmetrically. I was both relieved and impressed with myself.

Next came the only part of the booking appointment which was painful. Having lined everything up to their satisfaction and called out various measurements to each other for noting, the radiotherapists needed to make permanent marks so that they would know where to aim their magic beams once they started my daily treatments: one on the side of each breast, one in the middle. It was a momentary, and pretty mild, pain. It was also quite an inky procedure, so there was some mopping up to be done.

You may have gathered that I have no sense of embarrassment or self-consciousness about having my boobs out in front of medics – or, pretty much, anyone else – even when one of them was reaching across my body holding up my breast with both hands while another did the tattooing. Neither do I feel any embarrassment when medics poke around my cervix (which had already happened twice during my breast cancer treatment). It was just as well, all things considered. I feel for women who do feel this self-consciousness, although I am confident that most medical staff would be kind and sensitive and do their best to put them at their ease. I feel angry at a society that makes women feel bad about our body parts, a world in which social media bans pictures of bare breasts but allows open racism, that frowns on public breastfeeding but thinks that violence makes good

TV, and that scrutinises women's looks and shapes far more than our talents or opinions.

The booking appointment finished with the schedule for the radiotherapy itself. Starting on Monday 13 February, I would attend Bart's every weekday morning to be zapped, and should be done by 11am. I hoped for minimal side effects so I could enjoy some late morning coffee meet-ups with friends.

13 February 2017 : Radiotherapy Day One

The number 56 bus runs from very near my house all the way to St. Bartholomew's Hospital. And a very pleasant journey it is too – through Dalston, to the Angel, through the intriguing mix of old and new that is the City of London, down to St. Paul's Cathedral and round the corner to the hospital. On the first day of radiotherapy, I set off in good time and arrived early.

I met the radiotherapist. She was cool. It turned out that she was the union representative for the radiotherapists (unions and lefty politics usually come up in conversation pretty quickly when I am the patient). We ran through the forms and questions again. If I had a pound for every time I have told a member of medical staff my date of birth, I could probably have bought a small pharmaceutical firm by now.

We also ran through the potential side effects of the treatment again. It seems that radiotherapy may cause my boobs to swell. Given the size they already are, I thought that a warning to low-flying aircraft might have been in order. I had visions of me going into the radiotherapy room but being unable to fit through the door to leave afterwards.

The radiotherapist had a list of my treatment times for the next four weeks. They were all on weekday mornings, as promised, but were at slightly different times each day, and were subject to change. Oh well, it was not like I was doing anything else.

For the first three weeks, the treatment would zap the whole of my right breast. In the fourth week, it would zoom in on the area where my tumour was. This should kill any lurking cancer cells in the area. It is reckoned that radiotherapy reduces the chances of the cancer coming back by half.

I got changed into the by-now-familiar gown in a little cubicle, then went into the treatment room when called, stripped off my top half and lay down on machine. The radiotherapists (by then, two of them) shuffled me about until the lasery things lined up with the tattooed dots. They then turned the room lights down, which made the atmosphere comfortable and relaxing. I checked whether it is OK to fall asleep. 'Yes,' they confirmed, 'so long as you don't move.'

Reassuring me that if I had any problems, I could wave and they would come to my rescue, the radiotherapists left the room. The machine whirred and buzzed and moved around a bit, all the time firing its magic rays at my right boob. After about ten very relaxing minutes, it was done. I could go home.

But I decided to do a couple of extra things while I was at the hospital. The treatment was quite likely to cause skin irritation, and being big-breasted, my underboobs were already vulnerable to that, so I went to see the nurses to ask about measures to prevent and alleviate the impending skin soreness. I came away with advice, several tubes of cream and some padding. The watchword of the next few weeks is 'Moisturise!'. I felt like Cassandra from Doctor Who.

My final stop involved taking the lift up to the cancer ward on the seventh floor, where those nice people from Macmillan provided free complementary therapies every Monday. I was going for a massage! And very nice it was too. It was the first time I had experienced a massage fully clothed, lying on my back on a reclining chair, but 40 minutes of attention to my shoulders, arms and legs was just what the doctor ordered. And just as a bonus, the lunch trolley did its rounds of the ward while I was there and I got some sandwiches, a banana and a coffee. Life was still good.

As Bart's is conveniently located a very pleasant walk from the London Metropolitan Archive, I decided that the exercise and the brain activity would do me good, so I strolled up there and buried my head in century-old documents for a few hours before going home. This is the latest stage of the crusade I mentioned in Chapter II to tell the story of Minnie Lansbury's life. Radiotherapy side effects tend to kick in after the first week, so I had resolved to do stuff like this while I still could.

24 February 2017 : Radiotherapy – Halfway Through

Two weeks later, I had reached half-time in my radiotherapy. I almost expected someone to run in with a tray of quartered oranges to deliver a pep talk, but no such luck.

Oddly enough, I was rather enjoying it. I made a daily trip on a bus that took less than an hour to a lovely hospital where I lay down on a comfortable bed while supportive, good-humoured and non-judgemental staff gave me a totally painless, non-invasive, ten-minute treatment. And despite cautions from others who had been treated elsewhere, I did not even have to sit around waiting. Every day, they treated me pretty much as soon as I got there.

Bart's has a series of rooms in its radiotherapy department, each with a Linear Accelerator (Linac) machine, and it has named the rooms after planets. At the beginning of the second week, I was in Saturn; for the next couple of days I was in Venus, which filled my head with a Bananarama song. You may be relieved to know that there is not a Uranus, not even for colorectal cancer patients.

I was not sure that I would keep enjoying it until the end of the four weeks though, as the side effects were beginning to kick in. As my breast slowly cooked, the sore, hot, red area was getting more intense and spreading more widely. And I was getting more tired.

Tip 1: Do not wait for the soreness to start before looking after your skin. Drink lots of water. Moisturise! But do not moisturise before your day's radiotherapy, as it confuses the Linac machine and interferes with the treatment. Your hospital can give you moisturiser. And while I am sceptical about many suggested vegetable remedies, the radiotherapists recommend cabbage leaves and aloe vera, as there is some science behind that.

Tip 2: Make an outing of your daily journey. You may have to travel some distance, and may be in and out of the hospital in 20 minutes, so heading straight home may feel a little dispiriting. I met friends for coffee and sought out hidden gems in the City of London, where

Bart's Hospital is located. I thoroughly recommend St. Paul's crypt café, the Museum of London, and the wonderful Postman's Park with its memorial to Heroic Self-Sacrifice.

Oh, and 20 February was #onedaywithoutus, a day to mark the contribution of migrants to society. Alongside native Brits, they have been contributing a great deal to removing my cancer and stopping it coming back.

7 March 2017 : So, What's Radiotherapy Like?

The room smelled of nothing. Really, nothing. At all.

I lay back, gown down, naked from the waist up but clothed from there down to my shoed feet. It was most remarkably comfortable. Even my raised arms got cushioned rests that not only bore their weight but also brought my hands together without a hint of pain or even effort.

Two sounds competed. One, the background whirr of presumably the air conditioning, the breath of which occasionally registered on my skin and made me feel even more comfortable, if that were possible. And two, the radio, one of those commercial stations with music that is pretty much guaranteed to offend no-one but will probably inspire no-one either.

'Un-break My Heart'. The disco version. That always seemed a grating mismatch to me. My memory tells me this was once a rather plaintive ballad, before it got pumped up into a funtime dancefloor filler mixed into a mood that no-one who really wanted their heart to be repaired would feel.

Un-break my heart ...

Then a third sound joined in: the two radiographers – that day, a man and a woman – speaking letters and numbers to each other rather like the dentist does to the dental nurse when they check your teeth. I needed to be adjusted a little. A polite request, then firm but gentle hands moved my torso a smidgeon to the right, their touch not intrusive or discomforting but simply adding to the feeling of being cared for.

Our best range of used cars is now available with 0% finance ...

The radiotherapists were satisfied that I was perfectly positioned, lined up with my tattooed dots and lines of green light projected through cross-shaped openings in the ceiling and walls and bisecting my body. They took their leave, withdrew to their control tower (OK, more of a cubicle than a tower) and pressed the Start button.

The third sound now was not the radiotherapists' voices but the buzzing of the Linac machine. If I had wanted to open my eyes, I would have seen a big metal disk a few dozen centimetres above me and to my left, with a window in the middle showing its innards, and bolts and cross-headed screws holding its various bits in place. It looked like it was hovering above me like some device in a sci-fi film, but it was actually attached to a huge machine that stood granite-like behind my head, cradling me while its disk-doctor went to work.

Ten o'clock. The headlines. Farce at the Oscars as ...

A loud buzz drowned out the rest of the inconsequential story and the disk moved round from my left to directly above my right breast. Occasionally I felt a tiny pin-prick type feeling, but that was no different to the little blips we all feel every day. Go on, stop what you are doing and you will feel one within seconds. I liked to imagine that each little feeling was a cancer cell's dying gasp as the Linac zapped it.

When I looked beyond the big metal disk, I saw ceiling tiles considerately decorated to look like sky and overhanging boughs. Just as I started to picture myself lying in a sun-bathed, lightly-breezed field, the radiotherapist returned and told me that we were done for today. It was all over, but we would do it all again tomorrow.

8 March 2017 : International Working Women's Day

The global celebration of women's struggles and rights was also the day before my final radiotherapy session. By this time, I was noticeably the worse for wear from the treatment, but I was booked to perform some poetry at Ealing Trade Union Council's evening shindig, and having performed at this gig the previous year, I knew it was going to be a corker. The fact that they had invited me back was a positive sign!

My good friend Eve had organised the event, and had done so for the last five or so years. A crowd packed in to the smallish but very welcoming West London Trade Union Club in Acton. In between some excellent speakers, films and music, I got to my feet, dealing with my exhaustion by splitting my set into two parts either side of the break.

As a poet who writes about real life, it was inevitable that I would write about the experience of having breast cancer. I had first done so just three days after my diagnosis at a Loud Women 'We Shall Overcome' gig back in October, with my quickly-written first breast cancer poem, 'Tumour Humour: Titter Ye Not'. That was a useful exercise in getting the issue upfront, as it were. This time, I had a more extensive repertoire, adding some jokes between the rhymes. The surgery gags had them in stitches. (Oh well, suture self.) The Big C material was sandwiched between my other poetic material, covering issues including self-harm, the murder of Jo Cox MP, things I would rather do than cross a picket line, and mostly hating Tories.

Several women spoke to me afterwards about their experiences with breast cancer, and the sense of solidarity restored my draining energy.

In the sub-header above, I refer to International Working Women's Day, well aware that the word 'Working' – a crucial part of its original title – has been quietly dropped over the century-and-a-bit it has been celebrated. But here's to the working women who are helping to see off my cancer: the big majority of the NHS staff who have treated and supported me have been women, from the receptionists to the nurses and the surgeons; the only exceptions I can think of being the GP, an anaesthetist and a couple of radiotherapists. Sisterly solidarity to them all (including the blokes).

Cancer Can't Write Poetry, But Poetry Can Write Cancer

Poetry paints life, cancer takes it
Poetry means it, cancer fakes it

Cancer can not write, create,
Feel or think, illuminate,
Wipe your brow, commiserate
You're fucking rubbish, you are, cancer
Not a writer, player, dancer

Bring nothing useful to the table
Can't tell a joke 'cos you're not able

Poetry can't kill cancer, true
As that is medicine's job to do
But it can cheer as cancer dies
Laugh in lines when cancer cries
Tell the truth when cancer lies
Take confession of cancer's sins
Speak your grief when cancer wins

Poetry can be frightening too
Poetry can unsettle you
Verse inspires but tumours don't
Poetry prevails but cancer won't

30 March 2017 : Oh Dear, It's Oedema

Three weeks after the radiotherapy finished, something rather alarming happened. There I was, minding my own business, watching telly, when my T-shirt suddenly became soaking wet, in a patch from around my right nipple downwards.

I remember something similar on the occasions when I had newborn babies and the milk gushed out in excitement, but this was definitely not milk. Ah well, I thought, chucking said T-shirt in the laundry basket (an excellent device: I throw dirty clothes in there and a day or so later they come back to my room clean). Fresh T-shirt on, I returned to couch potato duties.

An hour later, it happened again. Another change of T-shirt and a bit of a worry. But I cleaned up and it didn't happen again. Until the following afternoon.

So I rang the breast cancer nurse for advice. This really is a most excellent piece of NHS aftercare – you are given the mobile number of a nurse who helps deal with any issue or problem that comes up.

She had some questions for me: *What colour is the liquid?* Yellow and clear. *Does it smell at all?* No. *Is your breast swollen or puffy?* Yes.

Does your breast skin have the texture of orange peel? Now you come to mention it, yes.

Conclusion: it was oedema: a build-up of fluid under the skin as a side effect of the radiotherapy. A quick bit of Googling reveals that oedema is most common in legs and feet, and can also occur in brains, lungs and eyes. Where do I get it? My boobs. Which, to be fair, is almost certainly less unpleasant that having it in the eyes or brain. When, on a totally unrelated matter, I typed the French phrase *c'est moi*, my laptop auto-corrected it to *chest moisture*, which seemed rather appropriate.

I had been intending to go to a union meeting on that day. But the need to get advice on this, the pains that go with it, and – most of all – the prospect of an embarrassing leak midway through giving a detailed report or expounding some important point of industrial strategy knocked that plan on the head. I began to imagine similar embarrassing leaks midway through the various other things I do in my life: supervising my railway station ('Please stand clear of the, erm, leak'), popping to the shops, performing poetry, waiting for a bus, running training courses ... I would suddenly notice that no-one is looking at my face any more and know that the phantom damp patch had appeared again.

The oedema might go away on its own, but it might not. Swollen, leaky breast in perpetuity did not sound like an enticing prospect. Massaging the affected area may help. I followed this advice, only to find that when I did, the retained fluid shot out at quite a rate. With careful aiming, I was able to have a fair bit of fun squirting it around the room. Oh come on, what's the point of having an unpleasant side effect from an arduous treatment for a killer disease if you can't have a bit of harmless squirty enjoyment?

The nurse was going to discuss my oedema with the oncologist and ring me back. It could be a long-term thing, so a long-term strategy could be required.

In the meantime, I would continue to look after myself to the breast of my abilities. Feeling like something of a wreck, I turned to verse.

*

Roadside Breakdown

She has to pull up
as she's overheating
Her engine sputters
the dashboard's beeping

She's burning up and burning out
worn and way past her best
Struggled to get through
her last annual test

She's found it more arduous
as she gets older
She's ground to a halt
on the hard shoulder

Lifts her bonnet
and lets the steam release
Slumps down on her chassis
and hisses in relief

She lays by and calls for aid
but recovery is hours away
Even for a lone female
of a certain age

After a refill of chill water
and some time alone
she revs herself up
and makes it home

But next time
she reckons
The scrapyard
beckons

4 April 2017 : Can Prayer Cure Cancer?

After visiting the hospital to get my oedema looked at, I sat for a while in the small church of St. Bartholomew-the-Less, conveniently located on the way out of the hospital towards the bus stop. I am not a religious person, and I cannot even claim that it was an oasis of calm, as the sound of construction work blasted past the big wooden doors and bellowed around the nave. But I fancied a ponder on matters theological.

Bart's-the-Less is a chapel of ease, meaning a church building that is accessible to parishioners who cannot make it to the proper parish church (in this case, St. Bartholomew-the-Great). The clients and residents of Bart's Hospital, and their visitors, surely qualify. For clarity, there was one St. Bartholomew, who had one great church and one lesser one; rather than two St. Bartholomews, one greater in some respect than his lesser namesake.

It is, as are most places of worship, rather beautiful – unusually light due to its strikingly large windows, and its walls adorned with resolute plaques memorialising hospital staff through the centuries who saved many lives and then lost their own. I sat on the crimson cushion on the wooden pew. The only other person there was, I think, praying.

I can understand why people pray, particularly in dark times of their own (or their loved ones') ill-health. Quiet contemplation and reflection can bring perspective, peace of mind, hope that recovery will come or acceptance that it will not. I also appreciate that knowing that other people are wishing you well is good for your morale and therefore possibly for your prognosis, and when people call that 'praying' I find it a bit awkward but OK.

The problem comes when people think that they are communicating directly with an actual being who will cure my cancer. On the day that my oncologist told me that my cancer was gone and likely not coming back, one person messaged me claiming that they had prayed to their god and that he had cured me. Even religious friends of mine – including clerics – see such claims and are not pleased.

Thinking about a person facing The Big C, cheering him or her on, hoping for recovery with all your mental effort, is one thing (OK, it is several things, but bear with me). But claiming a magical cure delivered by the intervention of a divine entity is very different. I often ponder this when, for example, athletes thank God for their victories in races or matches. Does God the all-powerful really intervene in sports contests? While self-evidently neglecting his duties elsewhere?

A decade ago, the most scientifically-robust study thus far reported on its investigations into the power of people's prayers for sick people (*New York Times*, 31 March 2006). For six years, scientists studied 1,802 heart patients, dividing them into three groups: those not prayed for; those prayed for and told so; and those prayed for and not told so. Members of three church congregations unknown to the patients prayed for their recovery by name. The outcome? Those prayed for made no better recovery. Indeed, the patients who knew they were being prayed for had a significantly higher (59% vs 51%) rate of complications. The report's authors thought this might have been down to a form of performance anxiety – perhaps a stress-inducing concern to live up to the expectations of 'prayer pressure'.

I would like to ask prayer advocates this: If your god cured my cancer, then did he not also cause it? David Attenborough rightly insisted that if you credit God for the beautiful things, then you must also attribute to Him the African child being turned blind by a small, God-created worm in his brain. Stephen Fry said in an interview with Irish broadcaster RTE in 2015 that given the chance, he would ask God, 'Bone cancer in children? What's that about? ... what kind of God would do that?'. Fry was then investigated for a possible blasphemy prosecution. The all-powerful God seems to become rather fragile when challenged.

I also have to ask why, if God chose to cure my cancer, he also chose to let all those other people die from it – and why anyone would worship a god who did that. Either God can not intervene to prevent appalling suffering, in which case He is not all-powerful; or He can and chooses not to, in which case He is not all-loving.

I think of my good friends and comrades Rob and Brian, who died of cancer thirteen years apart, both at the age of 45. Neither blamed

God nor believed in Him. And while I understand why approaching death may draw some people to embrace the idea of an afterlife, Brian insisted to me that I did not let anyone say he had gone to Heaven, even – perhaps especially – to his two young kids.

Challenged by these questions and contradictions, religions have stock replies: God sent these things to test us; God works in mysterious ways; God gave people the responsibility to make choices. But, for me, none of these square the circle that good things that happen to you are God's doing but bad things are either your own fault or sent by God to test or punish you.

Brilliant tennis player Serena Williams attributes her success to her relationship with God. After winning the 2017 Australian Open, she explained that whenever she found things tough, she prayed and God helped her. It seems to me that whenever she found things tough, she thought, concentrated, considered, steeled her resolve, redoubled her efforts and thus got her game back on track. It is her choice to conceive of this as asking for and receiving divine assistance, but it is a shame to believe that an external deity has helped you when your own toughness, spirit and sheer talent has achieved that.

I feel similarly about the claim that God cures (some people's) cancer. Why do some folk have so little confidence in human values and skills that they attribute good news to the Invisible One even when this is (I hope) self-evidently ridiculous – for example, that God would pick sporting winners or personally cure my cancer? Somehow, our society denies people this confidence, this consciousness of their own power and the power of human solidarity.

Credit where credit is due. The National Health Service cured my cancer: the health promotion staff who made me aware enough to notice its signs; the GP who referred me; the radiographers who confirmed it; the surgeon who removed it; the anaesthetist who kept me asleep while she did; the nurses who tended my wounds; the pharmacists who gave me my medications; the radiotherapists who zapped my boobs; and the receptionists, administrators, cleaners, caterers and others who facilitated them to do all this. Praise be to the NHS!

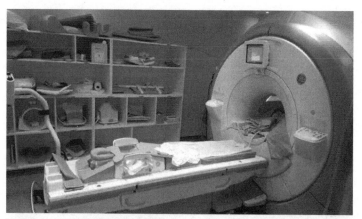

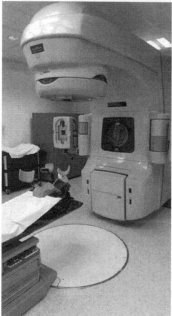 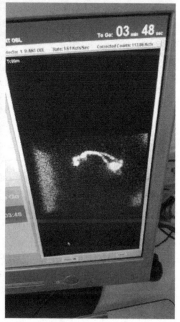

The technology of treatment.
Top: MRI scanner; bottom left: Radiotherapy machine;
bottom right: Nuclear scan.
[Photos courtesy of the author]

V

GETTING OVER IT

7 April 2017 : Back to Work

Less than six months after I worked my last shift before going off sick, I returned to duty in my proper job, as a London Underground 'Night Tube' station supervisor. These days, the official title is 'Customer Service Supervisor', but I prefer it if you have some idea of what I actually do – supervise a station – rather than imagining that I am some kind of whip-cracker in the complaints department.

I must be one of very few people to have a cancerous body part that rhymes with their job: Night Tube, right boob. I suppose there may be a cladder unfortunate enough to have cancer of the bladder.

That last shift had been on Halloween weekend, when one of the toughest challenges was distinguishing the passengers who were actually injured and bleeding from those who were simply wearing gory make-up. I had been working on London Underground stations for twenty years, and I would not have stuck at it if I did not enjoy it and value it. But cancer surgery and follow-up treatment were not compatible with the demands of the job, so since the start of November I had been either off sick or carrying out 'light duties' (in my case, organising hosted visits by autistic people to London Underground). I had not yet fully recovered from the treatment, but I had recovered sufficiently to make a start at returning to work. And working in a job which has – thanks to the past efforts of the trade unions – 100% sick pay for up to 39 weeks, I had been able to decide when to return to work on the basis of my condition and not my income.

I had arranged my return to work at a 'case conference' a couple of weeks previously with my manager, plus a 'People Management

Adviser' (yes really), and my trade union representative (hello Julie!). Seriously people, be in a union: have a rep, plus the combined power of thousands of your workmates, at your side through the tough times. If there is not a trade union in your workplace, then as soon as you join one, there will be!

I asked for reduced hours on my return to work, which management agreed. So on my first night back, I worked the first three hours of my usual shift, booking on at my usual time of 22:30. It was lovely to be back with colleagues, helping the station run smoothly, waking up inebriated people who were napping on the platform bench, and chivvying others to their last train (the station I work at has national rail services that do not run all night as well as the Tube services that do).

I would be working the reduced hours for the next four weekends, then would review it with my manager to see if I am ready to do more. That period of time takes me past my next appointment with the radiotherapy oncologist and the usual six-week recovery period from radiotherapy. This phased return to work (without loss of pay) is eminently sensible, and is an example of a reasonable adjustment to my working conditions. As previously mentioned, I also do some freelance work writing, performing and training. It is not just direct employers which have to make adjustments. However you work – whether freelance, or for an agency, or self-employed, whatever – you are entitled to reasonable adjustments. At post-treatment poetry gigs, I asked to split my set into two parts so it would be less tiring. When I returned to teaching residential courses, I asked for the bedroom that was closest to the training classroom, so I could easily rest during breaks. If I had known about the automatic door at one of the training venues that opened quickly and rather aggressively into the right side of my chest, I would probably have asked for an adjustment for that too – but instead, I learned to step quickly to the left straight after pushing the button.

The law requires employers (and service providers) to make reasonable adjustments for disabled people – which includes those with, or recovering from, cancer – where there is a working practice or physical feature of the workplace that places you at a disadvantage compared with workers who are not disabled in the way that you are. It is your boss's responsibility to work out what adjustments to make, but I heartily recommend working out what you need and asking for it. Here are a few suggestions:

- shorter hours without loss of pay
- more breaks, with a comfortable place to spend them
- a quieter, less busy, less brightly-lit workspace
- not having to do heavy duties that aggravate your wounds or scars
- avoiding substances and environments that may cause infection
- paid time off for follow-up medical appointments
- dropping the silly performance and attendance targets

These all seem reasonable to me. Go for it.

The law does not define what it means by 'reasonable', so if it ever gets as far as a legal case, the Employment Tribunal will judge it on a case-by-case basis, taking into account factors such as the size of your employer (meaning how large the company is, not the height or girth of your particular manager) and the cost of the adjustment. Once again, a trade union membership card will come in very handy – it will entitle you to a representative by your side and legal advice if you need it. More importantly, a strongly-unionised workplace gives you and your workmates the power to enforce decent conditions. Just having that card may well be sufficient to make your employer behave.

Failure to make reasonable adjustments for a disabled person is unlawful discrimination. Hopefully, your employer will know this and will make the adjustments you need. If not, you and your union representative can remind your boss of the law. Failing that, and if things get really bad, you have the option of submitting a claim to an Employment Tribunal. Most trade unions will fund cases that they think have a decent chance of winning or are important on principle. One example of a successful claim of failure to make reasonable adjustments for a woman with breast cancer was *Burke v Clinton Cards* in 2010.

There are five other forms of unlawful disability discrimination against workers who have cancer. In some circumstances, these also apply to people who have had cancer in the past, who are associated with a person with cancer, or who someone thinks has cancer even if they don't.

I was fortunate (or well-unionised) enough not to face any of these:

Direct discrimination. This is when an employer treats you less favourably because you have cancer. In 2006, the Disability Rights Commission (which was absorbed the following year by the new Equality and Human Rights Commission) reported several cases of women who had contacted them about employer action that amounted to direct discrimination (news.bbc.co.uk/1/hi/health/5402554.stm), one of the most shocking of which involved a cancer charity withdrawing a job offer to a woman after finding out that she had had breast cancer six years previously.

Indirect discrimination is when an employer applies a provision, criterion or practice which appears to treat everyone equally but is harder for (in this case) people who have breast cancer to meet.

Discrimination arising from disability is when your employer causes you a detriment because of something that is connected with your cancer. In 2017, the Employment Tribunal awarded nearly £50,000 to Eimear Coghlan after finding that her former employer – the Hideaways Club in Kensington – had been guilty of both harassment and discrimination arising from disability. During Eimear's breast cancer treatment, her employer had: removed her adjusted working pattern without consulting her; forced her to go on sick leave at reduced pay; and had demoted her to a role with a lower salary.

Harassment is unwanted conduct that has the purpose or effect of creating an intimidating, hostile, degrading, humiliating or offensive environment for you, or violating your dignity. Ring O' Roses nursery was found guilty of harassment of nurse Janet Bryant when the boss sent her false breasts after her surgery as a 'joke'. Ha bloody ha.

Victimisation is when the employer causes you a detriment for asserting your rights, e.g. if you make a complaint about any of the above forms of discrimination and the boss then treats you badly.

At the time I was writing this, workers had to pay to lodge a Tribunal claim, thanks to the Tory-LibDem coalition's disregard for the basic right of free access to justice. Fortunately, a legal challenge by trade union Unison got the charges scrapped.

Back at the proper job, I reviewed my annual leave entitlement and was rather pleased to see how much time I would have off during the rest of this year. The leave I was supposed to take while I was sick had been accrued and reallocated to later in the year, in addition to the leave I was scheduled to have this year anyway. I may only just have come back, but it would not be long before I would be off again. Nice.

Even the reduced shift, though, left me feeling knackered. This was going to be a long process. I was planning on returning to the gym and the swimming pool that week, and then to yoga and cycling shortly after. I had a plan. I had rights, I had solidarity from my workmates and I had a powerful trade union. But I still had pain.

11 April 2017 : Working Out Towards Recovery

Six months after I 'froze' my sports centre membership when I was too biopsied to work out, the day came that I felt thawed enough to unfreeze it. Yes, I returned to the gym.

It was good to be back. The familiar smell of foam mats, body odour and attempts to disguise it; the row of TVs with subtitles; the queue for the drinking water; and the motivational tunes: Skepta was going to get me exercising. It was good to get my muscles moving and endorphins flowing, and it was good to get back to another thing that I used to do before cancer so rudely interrupted my routines.

Returning to the gym after six months' cancer treatment gave me measurements of the deterioration of my physical fitness that I was already aware had taken place. Where I used to pedal at level 7, I could now only sustain level 3. The stretching machine which would hold my leg at a hundred-degree angle could now only take it to eighty degrees. And even without a way of precisely measuring it, I could feel in my bones that my bendiness was significantly less bendy, and my flexibility was down to about the level of a stick of rock. It was a very good job that the clientele of the gym I go to is very diverse, from the Greek gods bench-pressing to hone their already perfectly-honed figures to the noticeably out-of-shape doing a bit of light movement to stop themselves seizing up altogether.

My physical weakening had been one of the more dispiriting aspects of the cancer experience. Perhaps that may surprise you: surely the life-threatening illness, the invasive surgery, the waiting for test results, the painful side effects were worse? Maybe I am odd – actually, certainly I am odd – but I took that stuff in my stride. The enforced couch potato lifestyle, on the other hand, had left me so aware of my lack of exercise that I could almost feel the tone departing from my muscles and the energy draining from my body. I had become a jellyfish, without even the fun-looking trailing stingy bits.

I may have given the impression that before cancer I was, if not an actual body-builder, then at the very least, passably fit. The truth is that I have always been overweight and unfit, and was now more so than ever. The gym workouts – along with swimming and yoga – had been my way of stopping poor fitness descending into morbid slobbishness. It had kept me at a level of fitness just above the bottom of the pool. It was my safety net, and for six months, it had not been there. I had previously had a fourth method of exercise – cycling – but I had to stop that two summers previously when I broke my ankle stepping into a well-camouflaged hole at a festival, totally sober. It had taken fourteen months and surgery to sort out that particular injury (there were complications, not least of all long waiting lists and NHS understaffing). In fact, it was the day after I got the all-clear for the ankle that I found out that I had cancer. Way to go, timing gods.

So when I announced on social media that I was back at the gym and friends cried in alarm that I must not overdo it, I quickly reassured them. Never fear, good people, there was seriously no danger of that. Even before cancer, I was one of those gym-goers who puts on the gear and takes a smartphone and a good book to read on the seated bike. In fact, I posted said social media update from said seated bike. True to form, membership restored, I resumed my old habits and got through several WhatsApp conversations and a chapter of Bryony Gordon's *Mad Girl* whilst pedalling. I am sure it was just a coincidence that I was at the time reading this particular book, in which a woman describes her health struggles and eccentricities in great detail and with flippant humour.

I think this was when I figured out why the loss of my exercise routine had dispirited me more than being staple-gunned, cut open or cooked from the inside. It was because I could have done better. I could have done more exercise, both before and during my cancer treatment; I could have eaten less and more healthily; I could have looked after myself more effectively. Excess weight increases cancer risk and increases oedema risk. That other stuff – the surgery and so forth – I have no control over. That was easy to face: my own weaknesses and shortcomings were less so.

Never mind. I did half an hour on the bike, lots of stretches, and plenty of weights reps with my legs. Upper-body working-out was rather more cautious and less strenuous, due to the surgical scars, sore skin, oedema and such like, but I did some. I did an hour altogether. I knew that as I kept this going, my rusted joints would loosen and my flaccid muscle tone would slowly return. I may even get fit.

I pondered on my bruised, stretched, punctured, cut, scarred, reshaped body. It has so many stories to tell, so much resilience and so much beautiful disfigurement. I resolved to write a poem about this. Since the op, my creative brain had been preoccupied with writing verses on the subjects of World Mental Health Day, the NFL players' protest against racism and Harvey Weinstein's supposed sex addiction, but now its attention returned to my body.

Telling Time

My body is a timeline
with every thick and fine line
marking a milestone
time-grown
Each tract and fracture
captured
and preserved
a chapter
in each roll and curve

My belly tells
in its size and its hide
of what's been going on inside
The etched-on stretch marks
like a birch's bark
silvered and faded
since they first displayed
dark and light
raw and ripe
like a tiger's stripes

Between the moles
are the sealed-up keyholes
through some of which
a cyst was whipped
through others an ankle
healed
For which I feel
forever thankful

A line on my cheekbone
no longer a weak bone
Fortified
with titanium inside
An acrylic eye
that doesn't see
and doesn't cry

Excess weight
and childbearing hips
Bitten nails
and hair on my lips
Three little dots
for the treatment machine
Scars along folds
that are rarely seen

The biggest and best
a story scored along my breast
a similar size but a different shape
A valley in the landscape
a permanent monument
a tough white groove
from where the healing hands removed
the tumour that was killing me
and let me be

And every mark has a tale to tell
of getting fixed
and getting well
of being loved
of coming back from hell
A tale of off-centre
adventure
of trips and falls
friendships and brawls
scabby knees
from climbing trees

No tattooist's needle
is needed
to write my story
on my skin
to fill it in
to join the dots
and spots and pores
and wrinkles
Instead, life inks
and draws

If
by the age of fifty
my body by this stage
were still a blank page

I'd know I hadn't lived
that life had not yet given me
those rips and scratches
and snatches of excitement
delights and occasional frights
If nothing had changed
and no scars remained
Nothing ventured
nothing lost
nothing gained

My body is a timeline
It's mine
My life's storyline

16 April 2017 : Overdoing It?

Since resuming my membership of the sports centre five days previously, I had visited every day – and no, not just to check the timetable or use the vending machine.

A couple of days after returning to the gym, I reached untold heights of pleasure by swimming for the first time since before my breast ceased to be watertight and fully encased in skin and began its six months of being pierced, sliced, stitched, infected, creamed, irradiated, peeled and cooked. The wounds were still sore but they had sealed themselves up, so there was no risk of swimming pool water and/or germs getting in through fissures in my skin, nor of bits of my boob leaking out into a communal, municipal facility. Just when you thought it was safe to go back in the water – it was!

Immersion and movement in a body of water is surely the nearest thing to corporeal heaven here on Earth. Maybe it is the floatiness, maybe the coolness, maybe the luscious sensation of water streaming over skin or muscle pushing water backwards as water propels body forwards. Whatever, I loved it so much that I overdid it, and the next day my pectoralis major and teres minor were paying the price. At least I think it was them. I am no expert on the muscles of the armpit and boob, but I did know that they hurt. And my boob seemed to be expressing solidarity by shooting some well-aimed pains. Too much breast stroke, if you please.

But no matter. Nothing was torn, no wounds reopened, no real harm done. Maybe thirty lengths had been a bit excessive, but it was all part of getting back into shape and I was glad to be back.

Meanwhile in the gym, I had a new strategy for the arm-operated weights machines: do not have any weight on them. None at all. Pull out the pins and do some easy lifting. Movement is more important than load-bearing or resistance at this point, and frankly, the state I am in, just lifting the handles was quite heavy enough.

21 April 2017 : Back at Bart's

Six weeks after my radiotherapy had finished, I was back at Bart's for my follow-up appointment, to check how I was coping with the treatment and any problems I might have had since. The appointment can be summarised thus: *Hi. How are you? Show us your boob. Oh, that looks great. See you in December. Bye.* (I may have had encounters like this in the past, although not with doctors.)

Please do not infer from this summary any dismissiveness or rush on the part of the doc. Rather, infer the splendid news that I was heading at a rapid rate towards the light at the end of cancer's tunnel. Marvellous oncologist Doctor Wolstenholme checked me over, reassured me that everything was healing just as it should and that the oedema was on its way out. She was mightily impressed with my tales of my randomly-leaking nipple and squirting antics. I got the feeling that oedema does not usually happen this way. Once again, my breasts function in a very different dimension to the average mammary.

She told me that I did not need to use medicinal cream on my underboobs any more, that regular moisturising cream would do. With pretty much all soreness gone, my skin's appearance – in particular its darker and lighter patches – would fade to normal over the next few months. There were still lumps and bumps around my scar, but that was to be expected. Some of it was the remnants of the oedema and some of it was scar tissue. The remaining swelling would go away of its own accord, but the breast would always have its own unique post-surgical lumpy landscape.

I would have a check-up appointment in six months' time, open-access follow-up and annual mammograms. I felt safer than if I had never had breast cancer, in which case I would have mammograms only every three years. And with that, the appointment was done.

The following month, I was due to have an appointment with the surgeon at Homerton Hospital, and from then on, I would be an ex-cancer patient – monitored from a healthy distance but with cancer placed firmly in my past.

From the hospital, I went straight to a yoga class – my first since before my surgery. The opening five minutes were great: lying flat on my back, relaxing any tense muscle I might have, breathing slowly to the soothing tones of the instructor's voice.

Then it got tougher. A yoga instructor will always ask at the start of a class if anyone has any injuries, so I explained and was fully excused when I spent rather more of the following hour in child's pose than in downward-facing dog. The grey-bearded pensioner with the knackered knee doing yoga for the first time did more of the poses than I did. But I did not care. I was back. Strength and flexibility would return with time. In the meantime, I could hold the corpse pose for hours.

Brave warrior, me.

28 April 2017 : Behind the Headlines – Tories' Cancer Drugs Fund Exposed as Rip-Off

Today's headline was that the Cancer Drugs Fund (CDF), which had been announced by the Conservative-led government in 2010 and ran until 2016, was a 'huge waste of money' (bbc.co.uk/news/health-39711137). *The Annals of Oncology* journal had published a study led by Professor Richard Sullivan of King's College London, who also described the Fund as a 'major policy error'.

The Conservatives thought they could pick up a few votes in 2010 by promising to fund expensive cancer drugs that the NHS was not funding, and the CDF was the result. It funded cancer patients to receive medications which had not yet been approved by the National Institute of Health and Care Excellence (NICE). Launched in 2011 with a budget of £200 million, the Fund was supposed to be a stopgap while alternatives were developed, and was initially scheduled to run until 2014 (england.nhs.uk/wp-content/uploads/2013/04/cdf-sop.pdf). However, the government did not pursue its alternative policy, the ominous-sounding Value-Based Pricing, and instead extended the CDF until 2016, by which time it had been denounced by the Cancer Taskforce and the National Audit Office as unsustainable, and some doctors – including Sullivan – were calling it an 'unethical fix' and a 'waste of public money'. Still the Conservatives promised in their 2015 election manifesto that 'We will continue to invest in our lifesaving Cancer Drugs Fund' and issued a campaign poster with then Prime Minister David Cameron imploring LET'S FUND NEW NHS CANCER DRUGS – VOTE CONSERVATIVE. Just a year later, the Conservative government scrapped the CDF, absorbing it into NICE.

Sullivan's exposé dissected and discredited the Cancer Drugs Fund. Many media outlets reported its fall from grace, including the Tory-supporting *Daily Telegraph,* although it was careful to attribute it to the since-departed David Cameron personally rather than to the Conservative Party.

Around 100,000 patients received drugs under the CDF, but the study found that due to its failings, some patients were harmed by side effects ('dying in agony' according to the *Telegraph*), and only one in five patients received any benefit. However, that does mean that 20,000 benefited from the drugs they received. The study also told us that of the drugs with some evidence of benefit, the average extension to life was 3.2 months. Not only is every day of that precious to cancer patients and their loved ones, but as this figure is the average, some patients had extended their lives by considerably longer. One of these was Bonnie Cox, who had secondary breast cancer and had been speaking in public in defence of funding these treatments. Bonnie had been taking a combination of Herceptin and

Perjeta, the second of which was not yet endorsed by NICE and therefore only available through the CDF. She explained, 'I feel absolutely fantastic on these drugs. They have enabled me to carry on my life relatively normally since my diagnosis in 2015' (BBC TV interview, 28 April 2017). This combination of medications gives an average extra sixteen months' survival, which could make the difference between whether or not her son, currently two years old, remembers his mother. Her current drug regimen would continue, but after the scrapping of the CDF the planned next stage of her treatment was now in doubt. So while trying to live her remaining life to the full, Bonnie would now have to fight for the treatments that would enable that to happen.

In its five-year lifespan, the CDF cost £1.27 billion. Unhelpfully, the BBC lists 'Five things £1.27 billion can pay for in the NHS (over five years): 10,000 nurses; 2,500 hospital consultants; one of England's 10 regional ambulance services; a one-off pay rise of 2.5% for every member of NHS staff; an extra 20 GP surgeries' (bbc.co.uk/news/health-39711137). Report author Prof Sullivan dislikes this approach, criticising it in a TV interview on the day of his report's release as an attempt to trade off precious extra time for people with terminal cancer for other parts of the NHS. How far down this route will we go? Will we be working out how many tooth extractions would cost the same as a heart bypass operation? Or whether paying hospital cleaners a living wage would mean having to close a certain number of accident and emergency departments? The issue is not about robbing Petra to pay Paula, it is not about the purchase of extra months of life being a waste of money, it is about funding treatments directly and effectively – which, according to this study, the CDF did not do.

The case for a fund like the CDF arises from the length of time that NICE takes to approve new drugs, and its habit of rejecting some beneficial ones on the grounds of cost. Perjeta had been approved by NICE late the previous year, but only in combination with other drugs and for 'patients with HER2-positive, locally advanced, inflammatory, or early-stage breast cancer at high risk of recurrence'. It therefore remained unavailable to many women with terminal breast cancer through normal NHS routes. Moreover, having rejected it in 2013, NICE only approved Perjeta three years later when its manufacturer Roche agreed to apply a discount (nice.org.uk/guidance/ta424/chapter/2-The-technology). Its normal price is £2,395 per 420mg vial (excluding VAT); the level of discount is 'commercially sensitive', even though it is a deal with the Department of Health and therefore supposedly accountable to the public.

The Department of Health was unable to reach a similar discount deal with the same manufacturer for the life-extending medicine Kadcyla, leaving women with terminal secondary breast cancer unable to use it to extend their lives because of the £90,000 price tag. In 2014, Breakthrough Breast Cancer described Kadcyla as 'a brilliant drug' (*The Guardian*, 8 August 2014) but 'incredibly expensive', adding that 'Prices set by the pharmaceutical industry for impressive, life-extending drugs such as Kadcyla must come down. It's impossible to put a price on life's precious moments. But it's not impossible to put a fair price on drugs'.

When NICE refused to approve a drug, the only route to get it was through the Cancer Drugs Fund, which would, if you were lucky, pay the higher price. Four facts tell an important story about what the Tories' CDF was about:

1.	Before the 2010 General Election and the subsequent launch of the Cancer Drugs Fund, Roche threatened to pull out of the UK because it was not being paid enough for its liking (*The Guardian*, 11 April 2010).

2.	Roche's chief executive and lobbyists were heavily involved in designing the CDF.

3.	Roche was the greatest beneficiary of CDF spending (in 2014, around a quarter of all applications to the fund were for Roche's Avastin alone).

4.	Roche made a core operating profit of £18 billion in 2016 (roche.com/media/store/releases/med-cor-2017-02-01.htm).

The Cancer Drugs Fund was a mechanism for channelling public money into private companies' profits when a public body had decided that the price tag was too high or when the drug was not even effective. Professor Sullivan's study found that only 18% of drugs listed by the CDF met internationally recognised criteria for clinical benefit. The Fund was a facilitator for firms which marketed unproven products or over-priced good ones to be paid their over-the-top prices anyway.

Of course, if you are dying of cancer, you want the drugs, whatever the price. And of course, cancer charities will advocate for the provision of these drugs. My friends Rob and Brian both raised money to take trial medications and treatments because the doctors said that there was no more that the approved ones could do to stop them dying. If my cancer comes back and is more aggressive, even terminal, I will want to try drugs – even as-yet-unproved ones – and will be sickened if the NHS will not pay for it. The private companies are exploiting the desperation of the dying in order to up their profits, and through the CDF, the Tory government had been helping them to do so.

Today's statement from the Conservative Party praised the CDF and concluded with the mantra that NHS investment is reliant on a growing economy, which only the 'strong and stable' leadership of Theresa May could provide. The emerging truth about the Cancer Drugs Fund told a different story. While the Conservative Party claimed to champion access to cancer treatments, the previous year the Tory-led government had quietly 'de-listed' 25 cancer medications (*Telegraph*, 12 January 2015), a decision described by charities as 'a dramatic step backwards'. What chance is there of new cancer medications under a Tory government when it is withdrawing existing ones?

This day's headlines told of a failed Conservative policy, where a vote-grab was not backed up by proper resources or democratic accountability. That was bad enough. But looking behind the headlines, we can see something even more poisonous than the opportunism and incompetence that this suggests. It is the symbiotic relationship between the Conservative Party and big capital, in which cancer patients' lives are just pawns in a profit-maximising game.

If the government stopped kowtowing to pharmaceutical companies and instead brought them into public ownership, then it could develop and provide life-saving and life-extending medications itself, far more fairly and efficiently than the Cancer Drugs Fund or any alternative arrangement that lines the same pockets through a different mechanism. Until then, we could at least judge the Conservative Party on its now-exposed record.

3-4 June 2017 : Hot Boobs and a Weekend in Hospital

I had left my blog alone for some time, I suspect because I had been trying to see myself as Woman Without Cancer, ex-cancer patient, person with a past problem. Then that delusion blew up in my face (or rather, down my side).

Remember the oedema? The swelling and fluid retention continued, and after a few weeks, my boob began to get angrier. The red skin got redder, the dimples got dimplier as the swelling swelled, and the heat got so much hotter that the cat shifted her favourite snoozing spot from the middle to the right side of my chest to indulge in its additional warmth. And whilst the fluid that I had been 'manually draining' (squirting) previously had been yellow, clear and odourless, it was still yellow but now cloudy and smelly, surely indicating an infection. The usual lotions were not working, and EasyJet confiscated my Aloe Vera gel when I headed off to Barcelona for a couple of days.

I needed advice. Googling 'hot boobs' was not an option, for the same reason that ornithologists are wary of searching for 'great tits'. So I called my breast cancer nurse and headed to the Friday clinic at Bart's. The nurse said, 'Ooh, that looks nasty, you'll have to see the doctor,' and the doctor said, 'Ooh, that looks nasty, you'll have to see the consultant – next week.' As it turned out, the appointment with the consultant was more than a week away, and in the intervening time, the infection became even angrier: pretty darned furious, I'd say. It was when I started shivering and feeling dizzy on my way to work that I realised that as soon as I got there I would have to book off sick.

My next stop was Homerton's Hospital's A&E on a Saturday morning, where before I even got to the reception desk a big sign blasted out a warning that people who had recently had radiotherapy or chemotherapy were vulnerable to something called sepsis, which can kill you. Crikey, I don't remember being told that before, although I guess it might have been on the long list of scary side effects of which I had previously signed my acknowledgement.

Doctors and nurses prodded, checked vital signs, removed blood from my arm and stuck a cannula in the needle hole as they clearly intended to take more out, put other stuff in, or both. And they asked questions: lots of them. Every time I met a new healthcare professional, he or she asked, 'Are you allergic to anything?' I took to replying, 'Only Tories.' To a person, they replied, 'Don't worry, you won't find any of those in here.' I felt better already. This was the weekend before the general election, and I was gutted that my infected boob had prevented me going out canvassing for Labour. I made up for it in the hospital, taking every opportunity and getting into plenty of conversations with people who were becoming ever more determined to vote to save the NHS.

I was admitted and sent to the Acute Care unit, wheeled in my bed in what felt like a somewhat regal experience. I suppressed the urge to wave condescendingly at people as I went by.

Don't tell the government, but there were several empty beds in Acute Care, doubtless for the perfectly reasonable purpose of being immediately available for people with acute medical needs, who do not usually book in advance or sit patiently on waiting lists.

After more checks and questions, I was given a blood-thinning injection in my tummy, dressed in a ridiculous pair of stockings, hooked up to intravenous antibiotics and told I would be in at least overnight. It was time to call home and order essential supplies: crosswords, fresh orange juice, paper, pen, books, phone charger and a falafel wrap. Oh, and my pyjamas and toothbrush. Annoyingly, I forgot about the earphones required to watch the telly, so puzzles would have to take priority over watching silent *Doctor Who*. A short while after my partner had delivered my emergency rations, I was wheeled off again, this time in a chair, relocated to a ward.

All that remained to do was rest, be dripped into, take tablets, get driven nuts by all the bloody bleeping, and compose a poem, a follow-up to my current set-opener, 'Disaffected Middle-Aged Women'.

Disinfected Middle-Aged Women

A ward where women fight cirrhosis
Cysts or endometriosis
Battling germs with hourly doses
We're Disinfected Middle-Aged Women

Sutures, dressings and a clip
Special socks so we don't slip
En route to the loo with an IV drip
We're Disinfected Middle-Aged Women

Our eyes and wounds are prone to weeping
We're awake but rather would be sleeping
Because of that infernal bleeping
We're Disinfected Middle-Aged Women

We came here hobbling on the bus
We didn't want to make a fuss
But now they're mopping up the pus
We're Disinfected Middle-Aged Women

We're struggling with the bandage flaps
And half-filled cheese and onion baps
Bring yoghurt and falafel wraps!
We're Disinfected Middle-Aged Women

Bring crosswords or we'll get so bored
Put *Call The Midwife* on 'record'
And rename this the DMAW ward
We're Disinfected Middle-Aged Women

And if Theresa bloody May
Dares show her face round here today

She'll regret it – that's all I'll say
We're Disinfected Middle-Aged Women

We know the score, we're smart and suss
We'll tie the Tories in a truss
Save the NHS cos it saves us
We're Disinfected Middle-Aged Women

Then I noticed it: a huge and horrible wet patch spreading from my breast down my right side and onto the hospital bed. I hadn't been aware of it happening, but the infection had formed into an abscess, which had burst of its own accord, described later in hospital documentation as having 'spontaneously drained'. The well-oiled machine of hospital hygiene and care sprang into action, with the bed changed and me cleaned up in a matter of minutes.

The impromptu explosion had left a hole where the abscess had been, just below my nipple. This was not a mere dent or even a crater, but an actual hole, that I could peer into but not see the bottom of. When fluid formed over its opening, it bubbled. I couldn't decide whether it seemed more like a witches' cauldron or a sci-fi alien swamp – or whether it was scary or intriguing.

A good night's sleep would have been great. But after another dose of IV drugs, I was drifting off at about 2am when the young woman in the bed next to mine decided to phone her mother. Yes, really. This was the first night I had spent in hospital during my cancer treatment. Everything else, from surgery to radiotherapy, was conducted on a day visit basis: come in, have radical and life-saving treatment, go home.

When the doctors did the rounds on Sunday morning, I assured them that I was much better now, thank you very much, and I was sure that I would be fine if they let me go home armed with dressings and tablets. They agreed, and in the afternoon, off I went, armed with discharge papers that confirmed that I had in fact had the dreaded sepsis. It kills 30% of people who get it, so that's another of my many lives saved by the NHS.

Oh, and an amusing anecdote ... My eldest son was at a festival whilst I was in the hospital and texted that he had just seen the legendary John Cooper Clarke. I texted back the title of a JCC poem, 'Get Back On Drugs, You Fat Fuck'. Only I didn't send it to my son, did I? Oh no, I sent it to my breast cancer nurse, rapidly followed by a grovelling apology. Fortunately, she saw the funny side.

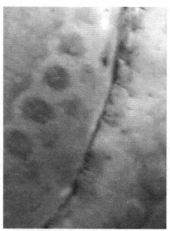

Battle wounds and battle scars.
[Photos courtesy of the author]

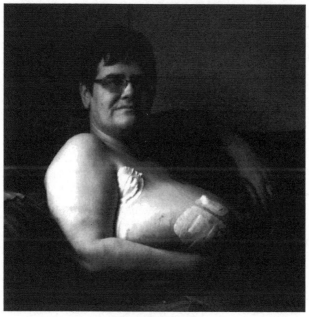

Brave warrior, me.
[Photo © Natansky.co.uk]

VI

KEEPING CANCER AT BAY

14 August 2017 : Whipping It All Out

You may remember that back in January, the medics discovered something dodgy on my cervix. It turned out to be a cervical ectropion – nothing too serious, but it would need some investigation and treatment. (It is probably related to my having had endometriosis for many years, though fortunately, much more mildly than many women do.) I pondered what the point was in treating this ectropion thing. With all my child-bearing done, I don't even need a cervix any more.

Then I remembered the long list of Tamoxifen side effects, and that it included increased likelihood of uterine cancer. That's annoying, I thought: I don't even need my uterus any more.

Then I found out that having your ovaries removed reduces your chance of breast cancer coming back. That's interesting, I mulled: I don't even need my ovaries any more.

You can see where I'm going here, can't you? I had a brief discussion with the oncologist, who confirmed the cancer-related facts. I suggested that a hysterectomy would be a good idea. With my uterine cancer risk raised, I was pretty sure that I knew a way to reduce it to zero: don't have a uterus. Plus, I could do without treatment on something I don't even need, and I could certainly do without my breast cancer coming back. I was not seeing any downside to this idea.

'Sounds sensible,' said the onco, 'but you will have to discuss it with a gynaecologist.' 'Can you refer me?' 'No, only your GP can do that.' At this point, NHS waiting lists (and a GP surgery cock-up) kicked in, and the gynaecologist appointment was eventually booked for mid-August. The gynaecologist agreed that yes, it is a good idea, and no, there is no downside other than the usual risks of general anaesthetic and possible prolapse.

The surgery was booked for 5 October. I would be having a full hysterectomy (ovaries, uterus and cervix), and believe it or not, they could do this by keyhole surgery. Impressive or what? Through the little incision holes, they would cut all the connections holding my bits in place and then deliver them through the vagina. There was a bit of a chance that would not work and they may have to open me up to do the job, but if that were to happen, they could just cut through my Caesarean scar.

8 September 2017 : Op Prep

Prepping for the op, the hospital needed to do an ultrasound scan. When they scan that part of your body, they use a full bladder as a sort of lens. So I was up at 07:30 drinking eight mugs of water, and expecting some discomfort (or desperation) as it worked its way through my system.

The scan revealed that I had a cyst on my right ovary, but that was pretty much irrelevant as the whole lot would be removed in four weeks' time. It was just another reason why this was a good idea.

After the ultrasound, I had the great relief of being allowed to empty my bladder, but then had to return for an internal scan, involving the insertion of a scanning device. Slightly uncomfortable. Not painful.

5 October 2017 : Hysterectomy, with a Little Hysteria

The alarm sounded at 05:00, I drank the two bottles of pre-op something-or-other the hospital had given me, reset the alarm for 06:15 and went back to sleep. I had only been in bed since midnight, after a delayed train journey back from a couple of days working in Glasgow, so when I got up again and went to the hospital for my hysterectomy, I felt like I could have gone to sleep for the operation without any assistance from the anaesthetists.

The nurse gave me the usual gown, a pair of tights with grips on the soles, and a pair of hospital knickers. What an absurd item of underwear these are. I refuse to believe that anyone is actually that shape.

I was number one on the surgical schedule, so I was soon wheeled off to the room where they send you away with the fairies. I've been through this routine six (or was it seven?) times before, so I am well used to it. I drifted off to controlled unconsciousness looking forward to waking up with it all over, maybe a little uncomfortable but sufficiently drugged up to feel relieved, relaxed and happy.

Sadly, that didn't happen this time. I woke up in the recovery ward with an overwhelming desire to go straight back to sleep and repeatedly did so, only to be woken up straightaway every time by an apologetic and concerned medic instructing me to take deep breaths. This happened over and over again, as the monitors showed a worryingly low level of oxygen take-up stubbornly refusing to rise. Accompanying this was a really very unpleasant pain, partly in my abdomen, partly in my lower back. I was already on the maximum dose of intravenous painkiller, so there was no way of reducing this.

Back on the ward, I was rather fragile emotionally and still in a lot of pain. The ward staff were run off their feet, rushing from one patient to the other with little time to listen to my moans. After having several requests for painkillers overlooked, finally I burst into tears. Then some powerful painzappers were forthcoming, and I began to feel a little better.

So, I had been having a really crap day when John arrived at visiting time. Somehow, I'm not sure how, he changed me from a blubbering wreck into my usual smiling, bantering, post-surgical self. Maybe it was because he brought fruit smoothies, puzzle books and WB Yeats without me even asking. Maybe it was just because he's a nice bloke. Whatever, he worked his magic. I don't want to be soppy or anything, but he really is something special.

The hospital staff had told me in advance that they expected to send me home the same day, but now they told me that the operation had been more complicated than expected and they needed me to stay in overnight. Apparently, my womb was in a pitiful state and it had taken well over an hour to get it out. Poor thing: all that child-bearing, menstruating and endometriosis had clearly taken their toll. It was old and knackered and it had to go.

The pain was the result of the docs pumping me with air to assist with the procedure. Finding this out, I had visions of myself as Harry Potter's Aunt Marge, inflated and drifting over the suburbs. The trapped air even caused pain in my shoulders – some kind of referred pain from pressure on my diaphragm. By early evening, I was burping and farting my way back to comfort. The medium-range forecast was for high winds, so family and friends were advised to not strike a match anywhere near me.

I settled down to an evening in a hospital bed watching the football on the posable TV screen with the headphones that my knight in shining armour had brought in. I had hoped that this would be a distraction from the pain and discomfort, but a goalless plod between England and Slovenia was really not taking my mind off it. Harry Kane finally managed to rescue the game with a winner in stoppage time.

Before the inevitable sleepless night, I had endure the removal of the catheter and 'pack'. It had been nice not to have to use the loo all day, but the tube and bag can not go on forever, so out they must come. Having a catheter taken out has a unique sensation: a combination of pain, relief and faint nausea. And the 'pack'? That was a huge piece of fabric stuffed up my you-know-what which the nurse now pulled out, somewhat like a magician pulling out a string of flags. I thought it would never end.

I had lost a lot of blood during the surgery – not enough to require a transfusion, but enough to warrant a month of twice-daily iron tablets to restore my depleted haemoglobin. I could look forward to stools like lumps of haematite, threatening to crack the toilet bowl. And to make sure that the toilet gets its daily dose of iron, I have a bottle of laxative.

I may have had a bundle of annoyances, but now I also had zero chance of ovarian, uterine or cervical cancer, and a reduced chance of breast cancer coming back. And for that, it was worth it.

9 October 2017 : Lesions and Adhesions

I had left hospital on Friday with instructions to go to my GP surgery on Monday to have my dressings changed. There were three of these, each a little square of bandage over a small laparoscopy wound. These were the three slots where the keyhole surgery kit was inserted. One is on my belly button and has two stitches; and one on either side of my tummy with a single stitch each. Each also has a rather attractive mottled blue, red and purple bruise, the navel bruise being the most striking and aesthetic. Dressings removed, wounds wiped, new dressings applied, job done.

Waiting to see the nurse, I read my hospital discharge notes and Googled the various terms thereon. It revealed a picture of my insides reminiscent of a horror movie.

I had adenomyosis uteri, meaning that my womb lining had grown into the area between the lining and the outside of the womb. This caused my womb to enlarge, with doctors measuring the size in terms of how big it would be if I were pregnant. Mine was fourteen weeks. Crikey.

My fallopian tubes and my left ovary were normal, but they were about the only bits that were. My right ovary had a 3cm cyst. My cervix had a polyp.

I had various adhesions, where bits of my insides had stuck to other bits of my insides. These usually result from previous surgery, so I reckon that a cystectomy in 2002 and C-section in 2004 had left some sticky scar tissue in their wake. My rectosigmoid (the junction between the colon and the rectum) was attached to my side pelvic wall and back abdominal wall, to which my bladder was also attached. My omentum was attached to my anterior abdominal wall. I looked up omentum, only to find out that it is a layer of peritoneum, which left me none the wiser, so I looked that up too. The omentum (Latin for apron) is a flap of membrane hanging down from the bottom of your stomach. I felt pleased to know more about my omentum, or m'omentum for short: my world was transformed.

Disentangling all that in order to get my uterus, tubes, ovaries and cervix out must have been quite a task, especially as it was all done through those little keyhole incisions.

Meanwhile, I apologised to those of my blog readers hoping for breast updates. Medical necessity had made the blog's coverage move south for a while and little was happening up top. My boobs were healed and happy, hanging asymmetrically, and my right arm and shoulder were getting more flexible and less painful as time and exercise went on.

18 October 2017 : The Fading of Pain

Yesterday was my first day without painkillers since my hysterectomy twelve days before. Not my first day without pain, but my first day without pain that had to be killed.

Moreover, the previous day had seen my wound dressings removed, with no replacement needed, and permission given by the practice nurse to have a bath!

The flatulence had now returned to its, ahem, normal level. Rather like Ophelia, which was making its way across the Atlantic at the time, it had been recategorised from hurricane to mere storm. My partner – who had been bearing the brunt of the adverse weather conditions – sussed out that I may have been taking too much of the laxative syrup the hospital gave me (well, it did taste of honey), and lo and behold, when I stopped taking it, my guts stopped bubbling like a witch's cauldron.

Enforced idleness at least enabled me to finish revising my trade union's course on Cancer in the Workplace, and I was very happy with the result. Thankfully, so was the Education Officer, and I was looking forward to delivering the first of the new-look courses in the new year. I felt like I was turning adversity into opportunity by using my experience to help arm union reps to fight against working conditions that cause cancer and/or make life difficult for workers with cancer (or workers caring for someone with cancer).

Hysterectomy brings on the menopause, and although I had already started 'the change' before having the operation, it brought on the rest in one big, hot, sweaty, dizzy, puffy, cranky, hormonal go.

*

2 November 2017 : Maps of My Baps – a Year On

Another day at the hospital, this time having my mammaries grammed. Yes, it was nearly a year since my surgery, and to comammarate this anniversary, my boobs must be squeezed and scanned again. A trip down mammary lane. Enough of the mammary puns now, please.

The procedure itself was the same boob-squishingly hilarious process that it was last year. I noted to myself how matter-of-fact I was about these things now. It's part of life, specifically of life continuing.

I stood in front of the booby trap and was positioned by the radiographer. When she said, 'Take a step to the right ...' it jogged my mammary (sorry) of discos thirty years ago, dancing in formation to 'Let's Do The Timewarp Again'. At least there were no pelvic thrusts involved this time. 'This will be a bit uncomfortable,' she said, but it wasn't.

14 November 2017 : One Year On, Cancer Gone – But For How Long?

The day had come to celebrate the anniversary of my breast cancer surgery, by going to an appointment with the surgeon. Or, as it turned out, with the surgeon's fellow surgeon, a little less senior. Shame: I would have liked to have seen Doctor Parvanta to thank her for saving my life and sewing me up so beautifully.

The great news was that the mammogram carried out two weeks earlier had shown that everything was fine. The cancer had gone, departed, taken its leave, got a single ticket on the long train to nowhere. Hurrah. I will have a yearly mammogram to check that it has not returned.

A study published this week (bbc.co.uk/news/health-41928647) revealed that breast cancer can return up to fifteen years after being removed. Given that this investigation studied 63,000 women over a period of twenty years, I think we can be confident in its findings. All the women studied took hormone therapy pills (Tamoxifen or aromatase inhibitors) and were clear of cancer after five years, but over the next fifteen years, 10% of the lowest risk group and a scary 40% of the highest risk group had their cancer come back. At highest risk are women who had large tumours and/or cancer in the lymph nodes. I didn't have the latter, but did not know the figures that determine whether my lump – 3.5cm when it came out – counted as 'large' or not.

I had been taking Tamoxifen, which works by blocking oestrogen from feeding cancer cells. But in post-menopausal women, a type of drug called an aromatase inhibitor is more effective, so now that all my girly bits had gone, I was swapped onto this instead. Without ovaries producing oestrogen, my body produces it via the enzyme aromatase changing the hormone androgen into oestrogen. Aromatase inhibitors get in the way of that happening. My new daily pill-shaped friend was the aromatase inhibitor Letrozole.

It does have its side effects (of course), so I was to keep on the lookout for tiredness, pain, lethargy, hot flushes, etc, though how I was supposed to tell the difference between that and how I usually feel was a little perplexing. Slightly more worrying was the possibility of bone thinning. I am fond of my bones and do not want them to get thin or fragile, thanks. So I would be back at the hospital in December to have a bone density scan.

This cancer-fighting business just goes on and on, doesn't it?

Haiku: Menopausal Dryness

More intimate with
Intimate moisturiser
Than I'd like to be

18 November 2017 : New Breast Cancer Meds Approved

The news came out today that the National Institute of Health and Care Excellence (NICE) had approved two new drugs which will help women with advanced breast cancer (bbc.co.uk/news/health-42006609).

Ribociclib and *palbociclib* have been welcomed as 'breakthrough' meds which can prolong life and give women up to two years without chemotherapy. Both are suitable for post-menopausal women with hormone-receptor-positive (HR+/HER2-) breast cancer (which mine was) which is locally advanced or is spreading (which, thankfully, mine was not). Both are taken as a daily pill, and are used in conjunction with an aromatase inhibitor such as Letrozole.

Currently, 85% of women with this type of cancer do not survive for five years. These two drugs will reduce that figure, and will improve the quality of life of many women in their last years.

So far, so good. But the story of how we got to this announcement shines a light into a murky place ...

It started with the private pharmaceutical companies that developed the pills. Novartis developed ribociclib, which it calls Kisqali, and Pfizer developed palbociclib, which it calls Ibrance. The latter got its clinical approval back in February, but NICE refused to endorse it for NHS use because Pfizer was charging too much at £2,950 per treatment cycle. Since then, NICE and Pfizer had been haggling over the price tag, and had now finally agreed on a discount on the list price. The amount of the discount is 'commercially sensitive' and therefore secret.

Let's think through what that means in practice. For nine months, dying women were denied a medicine which could have extended and improved the quality of their lives, while a private company tried to extract as much money as possible from a government that was trying to save as much as possible.

In a further twist, it turned out that the initial development of the drug was funded by the public, through government grants to Cancer Research UK scientists in the 1980s. Then Pfizer took over, and after converting the original research into a marketable product, had spent this year trying to overcharge the same public purse that had funded the original work on its money-making medication.

Pfizer's revenues in 2016 were $52.8 billion – yes, billion – and its net profit in the first quarter of 2017 was $3.12 billion. And yet it quibbled over a couple of grand for terminally-ill women. Meanwhile, what Members of Parliament pay themselves in salary would pay for more than twenty-five women each to receive this drug, but the government agency NICE was not willing to pay the full asking price. For nine months they argued.

How many pounds either side conceded we cannot know, because it is 'commercially sensitive'. This means that it would cause economic damage if the level of the discount was to be revealed. How so? Might Pfizer's shareholders have thought that it had been too soft and gone down too low? Might its competitors have seen it as a green light to undercut Pfizer and go after its markets? Might women dying of breast cancer have thought that Pfizer was a money-grabbing predator making profit from their impending death? Sorry, can't answer that – it's a secret.

The government and Pfizer were just doing what governments and private pharmaceutical companies do. They do what the system demands. The problem is the capitalist system, although that does not excuse our two hagglers their inhumanity.

NICE's name defines it as a body with a mission to ensure health and care excellence. Highly laudable. *Nice* indeed. But in what looks like a Freudian slip, Reuter's news agency referred to it as the UK's 'cost-effectiveness agency'. That's not the same thing, is it? Healthcare and cost are two very different concepts, two very different priorities. Just think: if NICE had a more honest name, it could still keep the same endearing initials. NICE: the National Institute for Cost Effectiveness.

I thought of the Small Faces' song 'Here Come The Nice'. It's about drug dealers.

And I wrote this villanelle. It was published on news-related poetry website Poetry24 and in socialist newspaper *Solidarity*.

Eyes on the Prize

The Pfizer guys are haggling with the NICE
And while they talk, the cancer spreads again
You'll get your pills when they've agreed a price

You'll get your answer when they've rolled their dice
And dealt your hand out in their counting den
The Pfizer guys are haggling with the NICE

So just be patient, please heed our advice
At some point, they will tell the patients when
You'll get your pills, when they've agreed a price

Shareholders and Execs must get their slice
Your longer life lies with the money men
The Pfizer guys are haggling with the NICE

It's hard for them to make this sacrifice
Each penny off's a penny less for them
You'll get your pills when they've agreed a price

Nine months of talks to get the charge precise
Let's hope that you can stay alive till then
The Pfizer guys are haggling with the NICE
You'll get your pills when they've agreed a price

4 December 2017 : Let It Snow, Let It Snow, Let It Snow

It was most excellent weather for menopausal women. While others moaned and brought phrases like 'brass monkeys' and 'stone jug' out of hibernation, I was enjoying blessed relief from the hot flushes and night sweats. I walked down the Euston Road, surrounded by people in woolly hats, scarves, mittens and puffer jackets, with me wearing lightweight trousers and a T-shirt and yet tempted to take even these off. I envied my friend Satu, who had her menopause when it was minus-twenty degrees in her home country of Finland.

My family and I were playing dial tennis with the central heating thermostat. They turned it up, I turned it down. They said, 'But Mum, it's freezing!' I said, 'Put a jumper on! Wear gloves! Drink some hot chocolate!' I reckon that heating and aircon systems could usefully be calibrated with settings of boiling, hot, warm, cool, cold, freezing, ice age, and menopausal woman.

Very rarely will you find me indulging in advertising, but I must make a product recommendation. Invest in a chill pillow. They are so, erm, cool. Goodness knows how it works, but the gel carries away your body heat to goodness knows where, and your cheek transmits the glorious cold around your grateful body. And when I say 'cheek', please infer that it can be used in either a lying or a seated position.

I got one of those polite letters from the hospital today (my copy of their letter to my GP), beginning with the words *I saw this pleasant lady in the Breast Clinic* ... It informed me that I had undergone a hysterectomy with bilateral salpingo-oophorectomy. This was not the first time that a letter from the hospital had propelled me to Google, which, to my relief, told me that the double-barrelled word means that I had had both my ovaries out – which, of course, I already knew. I was now determined to use this newly-learned word in a poem, especially as it is too long for Scrabble. I eventually rejected the idea of rhyming it with mastectomy and instead wrote an acrostic – a poem in which the first letter of each line spells out the title word. Ooph.

Oophorectomy

Ovaries
Out
Plus
Hysterectomy, hopeful
Outcome: odds
Radically reduced
Ensuring
Cancer can't
Touch, take
Obstruct or obliviate
My many more
Years

7 December 2017 : Scanning Bones

Yesterday, I had a bone density scan, to ascertain how dense I was. Or how dense my bones were, anyway.

This was because my new anti-cancer pill, Letrozole, has an annoying tendency of thinning your bones. So the good doctors were checking to see whether it was doing that to me.

And if it was? Apparently, I would have to eat more cheese. Result. I love cheese. Would this mean I could get it on (free) prescription? I couldn't help but hope so. I would also be well-advised to do more weight-bearing exercise. At my size, I am tempted to think that all exercise is weight-bearing, but I didn't think I would get away with that. In any case, I was already a weight-pumping gym user, albeit of a rather leisurely kind.

I checked in at Homerton Hospital X-Ray 2, and the receptionist told me to sit in either waiting room. What? I wasn't expecting to have to decide between two waiting rooms! My washing machine brain went into spin-cycle, running through the various factors involved in this decision. Which looks the more comfortable? In which one am I less likely to not hear when I am called? Which of the two has the least distracting distractions? Which affords the opportunity to sit in a place which makes a symmetrical pattern with the rest of the room that is least likely to be disturbed by other people sitting down? Can't I just stand up in between them gawping rather than making an actual decision? I was still doing this when the radiographer appeared and called my name. Phew. Decision averted.

Said radiographer was a very nice young man called Rob. So nice that when he asked me the compulsory question *Do you suffer from chronic malnutrition?* he didn't even raise his eyebrows, let alone laugh uproariously. And I guessed he had not had time to look at my notes when he asked *Is there any chance you could be pregnant?*

Questions aside, the scan involved lying on a comfortable bed, top half gowned, lower half dressed, metal stuff removed from pockets. A scanning arm buzzed above me, my lie was adjusted a couple of times, and within ten minutes, my lower back and both hips had been scanned.

The scan would now be analysed, and I would get the result from my GP shortly. I have to say, though, that my hips looked great on the screen. And, you know, the hips don't lie ...

30 December 2017 : Skeleton Service – Dense Bones and Digital Disasters

Today I received the delightful news that my bone density was normal. It was a seasonal relief to know that I was not walking around on a skeleton on the point of snapping or dissolving. Phew. Hopefully, it would still be OK for me to take the sensible precaution of eating lots of cheese. You know, just in case.

You may remember that this test was carried out on 6 December, twenty-four days ago. Even allowing for the season of goodwill and postal delays, that seemed a long time to wait for a simple result of a simple test. Indeed, the letter showed that the result letter was generated on 18 December. Perhaps the 'twelve days of Christmas' refers to the time it takes to get a test result to the patient. The letter itself was a copy of a letter sent to my GP's surgery, which had been unable to tell me the result when I had phoned the previous week.

But hang on – wasn't this the twenty-first century? Why were medical test outcomes being notified by snail-mail anyway? It appeared that I was not the only person riled by this, as illustrated by the delightfully-named Dick Vinegar's festive moan in *The Guardian* four years previously (theguardian.com/healthcare-network/2013/feb/18/nhs-letters-email).

Although the impact on me on this occasion had not been of any great seriousness, it was not an isolated occurrence. Just before Christmas, I had been to a follow-up appointment with the cancer consultant at Bart's and found that she had no idea that I had had a hysterectomy. Why? Because it had taken place in another hospital and the information had not been shared. It is surely not beyond our capacity as a society to facilitate our National Health Service to use digital communication and information-sharing. In fact, I expect that beyond the initial outlay, it would save money and resources for the perennially cash-starved NHS.

So, why has this not happened? As is usually the case, a dip into the history of the issue may help to explain. A 2016 report by the King's Fund ('A Digital NHS') provides a useful summary of the background, which can be further distilled into a timeline looking something like this:

- 1960s: computers first used in the NHS for administrative, financial and research purposes
- 1970s: first Department of Health review into use of digital technology
- 1992: first national information technology (IT) strategy for the NHS
- 1998 and 2002: subsequent strategies, leading to the creation of the National Programme for IT (NPfIT), later called Connecting for Health.

The King's Fund report explained that Connecting for Health aimed 'to create a single electronic care record for patients, connect primary and secondary care IT systems, and provide a single IT platform for health professionals' and argued that 'this multi-billion-pound programme of investment dominated the digital agenda under the Labour government' but that 'it failed to achieve its main objectives – including establishing an integrated electronic health record system across secondary care – although it did establish some important national digital infrastructure and services'. It blamed overly-centralised decision-making and a lack of local engagement, meaning that users' needs 'were poorly understood and providers were directed to implement at pace systems they had little say over'. Connecting for Health formally came to an end on 31 March 2013, three years after Labour had been replaced in government by the Tory-LibDem coalition.

There were plenty of technical explanations of the failure of Connecting for Health, but was there also a political explanation? Tony Blair's 'New Labour' government had an evangelical belief in the all-round superiority of the private sector, and an equally evangelical determination to reject public provision as old-fashioned socialist baggage. So this programme, along with many others in the NHS and across the public sector, was hived off to private companies. And private companies, whatever their advertising says, are motivated by making money. That is the nature of the beast.

The programme divided England into five clusters, and gave them to private enterprises as follows:

- Computer Sciences Corporation (CSC) – North, Midlands & Eastern (NME) cluster
- BT Health London (formerly BT Capital Care Alliance) – London cluster
- Accenture – North East and East/East Midlands clusters
- Fujitsu – Southern cluster

However, by May 2008, only two main contractors remained – CSC and BT. Accenture gave up nearly all its involvement in January 2007, handing over its £2 billion workload to CSC but keeping a small hand in Picture Archiving and Communication System (PACS) rollout only. Fujitsu messed up so badly that its contract was terminated in May 2008. As so often happens, the private contractor had contracted-out large chunks of its work, in this case to software developers who apparently succeeded only in developing software that crashed.

Some parts of the Connecting for Health programme did work quite well, such as digital storage of X-rays and IT installation in GP surgeries. But the national network was an expensive failure, one victim among many of New Labour's obsession with inviting the private sector into the public. Even now it has been scrapped, the NHS remains tied into some of its contracts until the 2020s.

Now we had the Tories in power, and the appalling Health Secretary Jeremy Hunt had challenged the NHS to 'go paperless' by 2018. The target year started the day after tomorrow, and the challenge was not looking too likely to succeed.

Is it just me, or is there something rather odd about the person in charge of the NHS 'challenging' it to do something rather than resourcing it to do so? Or was this just the sleight-of-hand, target-and-tick-box culture that allows right-wing politicians to pretend that they support our NHS while they take it apart by stealth?

Hot Flush

by Donna How-I'm-Gonna-Cope-Come Summer

Sittin' here sweatin' my heart out waitin'
Waitin' for my temperature to fall
Tried about a thousand remedies lately
Want to bash my head on the wall

Gonna have a hot flush, baby, this evenin'
Gonna have a hot flush, baby, tonight
I don't want a hot flush, baby, this evenin'
Gonna need a flannel
Gotta need some ice tonight

                     (hot flush)

Lookin' to get myself out of danger
Don't want another night drenched in sweat
Wanna share my bed with a heat exchanger
Don't wanna wake up shaking and wet

Gonna have a hot flush, pantin' and breathin'
I can feel the onrush, gripping me tight
I can feel my hip joints achin' and creakin'
Got some cream to rub in
Plunge into the tub tonight

                     (hot flush)

Brain feels like it's slop mush, turn off the heatin'
Hair looks like a bog brush, terrible sight
Think I'm going to throw up, pukin' and heavin'
Hot flush, baby
Gonna need a flannel tonight

                     (hot flush)

Sittin' here achin' my joints out waitin'
Waitin' for my memory to return
Trying hard to figure out what my name is
I think I'm going to melt down and burn

Now I've got a spot of thrush, soreness and bleeding
There will be no hot stuff, baby, tonight
If I tell you to fuck off, baby, believe me
Better do a runner, or you're gonna get a fight

Don't wanna have a hot flush, baby, this evenin'
Don't need a hot flush, baby, tonight
Cookin' in my hot flush, baby, this evenin'
Tired and buzzin', baby, gonna need some sleep tonight

24 February 2018 : Hello Hospital, My Old Friend

I'd just got home from hospital. In the middle of last night, while I was at work, my right arm began to feel uncomfortable. My fingertips became numb and my arm cold and tingly. It was rather like those times when you wake up in the night and realise you have been lying on your arm. So I hoped that if I shook it about a bit and carried on regardless, the strange sensation would soon pass. So I did. But it didn't.

It wasn't sufficiently debilitating to stop me working the rest of my shift. But it was worrying. And it was very annoying.

So I finished work, headed home, crashed out for about six hours, woke up, still had the discomfort, got up, shook it about a bit, had a cup of tea, hoped it would go away, listened to the football, and was disappointed by both the result of the match and the fact that my arm was getting worse rather than better. So off I trotted to A&E at Homerton Hospital.

After a wait that lasted about three chapters of the novel I was reading, the nurse and then the doc had a good look. A blood test ruled out any infection. Prodding discovered that my lymph nodes were a bit on the big side, so the theory was that my oversized lymph nodes had tweaked a nerve.

I would have to go back to the hospital a week on Monday to a clinic which would arrange an ultrasound scan of my armpit. This was quite an entertaining prospect. I expected the experience to be something like having roll-on deodorant applied by someone else. The mind boggles.

In the meantime, I had to metaphorically sit tight and literally move about and exercise. And I had to be on my guard. The symptoms were thus far local: every tingle, cold feeling, numb patch and pain was located between my right boob and the fingertips of my right hand. Should I start having systemic symptoms, e.g. temperature or dizziness, then that might indicate an infection, and that would indicate the need to go legging it back to the hospital sharpish.

If it was what they thought it was, then it was not life-threatening or even particularly serious. But there was no simple way of sorting it out. It could involve long-term physiotherapy, it could involve long-term discomfort. And it was my writing hand.

It seemed that even when your cancer has gone, you never stop being a cancer patient.

2 March 2018 : Give Us a Clue

Cancer Research UK has ruffled some feathers with its campaign to publicise the links between obesity and cancer (campaignlive.co.uk/article/this-not-fat-shaming-cancer-research-uk-stands-anti-obesity-campaign-backlash/1458472), prompting accusations of 'fat-shaming'. I'm not easily offended – in fact, I dislike the whole notion of 'offence' – but the campaign does deserve some scrutiny.

Why do the campaign's posters centrally feature the word OB_S_ _Y? Why the missing letters? Why not just come out and say it? OBESITY.

Is it a puzzle? I've checked on crosswordsolver.org and OBESITY is the only word that fits. Perhaps they are just determined to make it tricky for people who don't use crosswordsolver.org (perhaps because they don't do crosswords) or who struggle with reading, English, or reading English.

Or maybe they are ashamed to print the whole word because they assume that people are – or ought to be – ashamed of being obese.

The fact that excess weight is linked to health problems will be news to absolutely no-one. Fat people get this message every day. If an advertising campaign could stop people being overweight, then we would be a nation of thinnies.

Or perhaps they think that there are fat people who don't care about obesity causing heart disease, strokes, diabetes, depression and the other problems that they already know about, but will suddenly vow to lose weight because of this revelation about cancer?

All this begs a more important question. Obesity may cause cancer, but what causes obesity? It's complex, but one factor is shame. So let's stop adding to that. Another factor is the vigorous promotion of unhealthy food by profiteering corporations. So how about aiming a campaign at them?

5 March 2018 : No 'Arm in Getting it Checked Out

When they released me from A&E last week, they pressed into my hand an invitation to the HAMU. It turns out that this is the Homerton Ambulatory Medicine Unit, a clinic that you walk in to. Is it just me, or is this an excessively wordy name – with an accompanying weird acronym – for what could just as easily be called 'Outpatients' or 'Walk-in Clinic'?

Anyway, I digress. For a walk-in clinic, it is not at all well signposted, so I ambulated around the hospital for some time before I actually found it.

I checked in, assured them that my birthday, address, GP, next of kin, et cetera, had not changed since I was last there nine days ago, sat as instructed in the waiting area and prepared for a long wait with a good book (*The Making of Her* by Susie Nott-Bower). However, I had barely read a single sentence when I was summoned to sit on a comfy chair in a curtained cubicle to be attended to.

The doctor got me to squeeze her fingers, prodded me and asked if it hurt, and checked out my armpits. Some examinations hurt, some make you scream, some make you wince. This one makes you giggle.

After the doc popped out for a quick consult with the consultant, she returned to give me the lowdown. My lymph nodes were a bit enlarged and have probably trapped a nerve. There was no need for an ultrasound. There was also no need to wear the sleeve that some women have to wear in this situation if they have swelling in the arm (which is a trifle disappointing, as I had been discussing with my friend Grace the possibility of designing some particularly cool ones). Instead, I left with just the reassurance that the pain, numbness and tingling will probably reduce over time, and an instruction to return if they do not.

'Do you feel relieved?' asked my partner that evening. Honestly, I didn't think I felt anything. Going to the hospital to get shit checked out is just the way I roll these days. It's part of life.

2 July 2018 : Cancer Takes Another One

Today I attended the funeral of another great friend – John – who had died from cancer one month before. His daughter's eulogy prompted this poem.

A Warm Hand

I wanted to clap at the funeral today
But I think that is seen as poor taste
I longed to applaud such a brilliant speech
But I feared it would seem out of place

I wanted to shout 'Hear! Hear!' when you said
Deceased was a wonderful chap
The whole of me knew this was so very true
I was craving to let out a clap

I wouldn't have whooped, or whistled, or cheered
Or given a standing ovation
But your tribute was funny, and bang on the money
It deserved our polite acclamation

I managed to keep to a smile and a weep
And ensured that the tone wasn't ruined
But it will be fine if you all clap at mine
– Just hold back on the hissing and booing

21 November 2018 : That Looks Suspicious

Two weeks ago, I had my second annual post-surgery mammogram and the medics had found no signs of cancer on the day. However, a mammogram is not done and dusted until the proper specialist has had a good squint at it afterwards, looking intently for any cause for concern.

And so it was that last week, I got a phone call from the hospital asking me to come in today for a follow-up scan. In the days following, this was followed by a letter, another phone call and three text messages. They were certainly keen that I bring my boobs to the hospital today, and despite my usual nonchalance about the lemons that life might throw at my melons, I didn't sleep too well last night.

Today, I left the TUC Disabled Workers' Committee meeting early (having had a good sound-off about various items), and took myself to Homerton Hospital. Once there, it was a routine that I am well used to by now – the basket, the gown, the cubicle, and then another mammogram.

It turns out that the suspicious apparition on the first mammogram was in my left boob, perhaps jealous of the attention that the right one has received over the last couple of years. The radiographer hoisted the aforementioned boob onto the machine and asked politely if she might draw on it. Of course I agreed, so she brandished her pen. I had expected some special medical boob-writing quill, but it was a regular newsagent fibre-tip, remarkably similar to the one I had been using to fill in the crossword in the waiting room.

This time, they needed to take a closer look, which meant that they needed to squeeze my boob much tighter than previously. Once it was (finally) in position, the transparent plate was lowered on top of it, then down some more, some more, and some more, until what had previously looked like a loaf of bread dough on a table now looked more like a pancake.

This was repeated some half-dozen times until they had a whole gallery of snapshots of my left breast. During this process, I had been required to stand at some rather odd angles and actually, it did hurt. I even squealed a bit. Still, all in the line of duty.

A word to the NHS: you need bigger mammogram machines. Perhaps not for everyone, but certainly for some of us.

Mammogram done, I was then whisked off to the ultrasound room and another familiar procedure. This time, the specialist who had spotted the cause for concern was carrying out the scan, so I asked her to tell me exactly what was going on and she obliged. After the last two-and-a-bit years, no-one needs to worry about giving me bad news or scary information. I'd rather know.

There was a small shadow in the shape of two circles on the mammogram that hadn't been there the year before, so we had to have a good ultrasonic look at it. If it turned out to be suspicious then the next step would be the dreaded biopsy.

The expertly-guided, gel-covered, hand-held scanner slid around and pressed into my breast as I watched its progress on the screen. As TV shows go, it had a lot of suspense but not much character development and rubbish dialogue. Still, the scenery was fascinating, and the commentary very informative.

Then it appeared. Between the blood vessels, ducts and fat cells, there was a dark round thing. And next to it, another one. The fantastic news was that they were lymph nodes, of normal size, just getting on with doing their job. Worry over. No need for the dreaded biopsy.

In celebration, the doc showed me the mammogram pictures on her large monitor. Not boasting or anything, but my boob looks like a planet. Best of all, a cancer-free planet.

'See you next year,' she said.

Homage to Hospitals

All hail to public hospitals
Which treat us at no cost at all
Come forth and heed the homage call
Give thanks and praise

Admire their shiny corridors
The wonder drugs in well-stocked stores
And colour-coded wings and floors
And curtained bays

Where patients' injuries are healed
By specialists in every field
Equipment-laden trolleys wheeled
In urgency

To rooms where skilful medics stand
And scalpels rise at their command
You fall asleep in wondrous hands
In surgery

Cathedrals where the sick may throng
To scream and moan their evensong
To come out weak but then grow strong
With aftercare

So come ye to our hallowed shrine
Bring broken bones and twisted spine
Partake of medicines divine
Beyond compare

It's so much more than just a fort
This temple Branson thinks he's bought
The profit bug that he has caught
To cut and trim

So he can keep his filthy paws
Clean off our holy corridors
And keep our swinging theatre doors
Away from him

And recommit thyself from hence
To fight off foes, from where, from whence
Come form brigades in their defence
and give no ground

So stand your guard and don't relax
Be vigilant against attacks
From governmental cutters' axe
From snake oil salesmen, crooks and quacks
Let's raise our arms and watch our backs
And stop those bastards in their tracks
So when you've cuts or breaks or cracks
Your hospital has not relapsed
– It's still around